Daniel J.

Ciba Foundation
Study Group No. 35

CHEMICAL INFLUENCES
ON BEHAVIOUR

CHEMICAL INFLUENCES
ON BEHAVIOUR

Ciba Foundation
Study Group No. 35

Edited by
RUTH PORTER
and
JOAN BIRCH

J. & A. CHURCHILL
104 GLOUCESTER PLACE, LONDON

1970

616.8918
S 933

First published 1970

With 52 illustrations

International Standard Book Number 0 7000 1463 2

CONTENTS

* Contributed after the meeting.

★ This paper could not be read at the time of the meeting.

MEMBERSHIP

Study Group on Chemical Influences on Behaviour held 26th and 27th February 1970

E. Boyland . . Chester Beatty Research Institute, Royal Cancer
(Chairman) Hospital, Fulham Road, London, S.W.3, England

R. E. Albert . . Institute of Environment Medicine, New York University Medical Center, 550 1st Avenue, New York, N.Y. 10016, U.S.A.

J. M. Barnes . . MRC Toxicology Research Unit, Woodmansterne Road, Carshalton, Surrey, England

A. H. Beckett . . Department of Pharmacy, Chelsea College of Science and Technology, Manresa Road, London, S.W.3, England

R. W. Brimblecombe . Medical Division, Chemical Defence Establishment, Porton Down, Salisbury, Wiltshire, England

J. J. Cowley . . Department of Psychology, The Queen's University of Belfast, Belfast BT7 1NN, Northern Ireland

H. Harris . . . MRC Human Biochemical Genetics Research Unit, The Galton Laboratory, University College London, Wolfson House, Stephenson Way, London, N.W.1, England

M. Horváth* . . Institute of Industrial Hygiene and Occupational Diseases, Srobárova 48, Praha 10—Vinohrady, Czechoslovakia

C. R. B. Joyce . . Medical Department, CIBA D.B., 4000 Basel 7, Switzerland

S. S. Kety . . . Psychiatric Research Laboratories, Massachusetts General Hospital, Boston, Massachusetts 02114, U.S.A.

A. R. King . . . MRC Neuropharmacology Research Unit, Department of Experimental Neuropharmacology, The Medical School, Birmingham 15, England

A. Lewis . . . Institute of Psychiatry, De Crespigny Park, Denmark Hill, London, S.E.5, England

* Not present at the meeting.

MEMBERSHIP

E. Marley . . Department of Psychiatry, Institute of Psychiatry, De Crespigny Park, Denmark Hill, London, S.E.5, England

G. E. Paget . . Smith Kline & French Laboratories Ltd, Welwyn Garden City, Hertfordshire, England

J. McL. Philp . . Unilever Research Laboratory, Colworth House, Sharnbrook, Bedford, England

M. Sandler . . Department of Chemical Pathology, Queen Charlotte's Maternity Hospital, Goldhawk Road, London, W.6, England

A. P. Silverman . . Industrial Hygiene Research Laboratories, ICI Limited, Alderley Park, Nr. Macclesfield, Cheshire SK10 4TJ, England

A. Spinks . . Pharmaceuticals Division, ICI Limited, Alderley House, Alderley Park, Nr. Macclesfield, Cheshire SK10 4TF, England.

Hannah Steinberg . Department of Pharmacology, University College London, Gower Street, London, W.C.1, England

M. Tomkiewicz . Department of Pharmacology, University College London, Gower Street, London, W.C.1, England

P. H. Venables . . Department of Psychology, Birkbeck College, Malet Street, London, W.C.1, England

L. Weiskrantz . . Institute of Experimental Psychology, University of Oxford, 1 South Parks Road, Oxford, England

The Ciba Foundation

The Ciba Foundation was opened in 1949 to promote international cooperation in medical and chemical research. It owes its existence to the generosity of CIBA Ltd, Basle, who, recognizing the obstacles to scientific communication created by war, man's natural secretiveness, disciplinary divisions, academic prejudices, distance, and differences of language, decided to set up a philanthropic institution whose aim would be to overcome such barriers. London was chosen as its site for reasons dictated by the special advantages of English charitable trust law (ensuring the independence of its actions), as well as those of language and geography.

The Foundation's house at 41 Portland Place, London, has become well known to workers in many fields of science. Every year the Foundation organizes six to ten three-day symposia and three to four shorter study groups, all of which are published in book form. Many other scientific meetings are held, organized either by the Foundation or by other groups in need of a meeting place. Accommodation is also provided for scientists visiting London, whether or not they are attending a meeting in the house.

The Foundation's many activities are controlled by a small group of distinguished trustees. Within the general framework of biological science, interpreted in its broadest sense, these activities are well summed up by the motto of the Ciba Foundation: *Consocient Gentes*—let the peoples come together.

CHAIRMAN'S OPENING REMARKS: ENVIRONMENTAL CHEMICALS AND BEHAVIOUR

E. BOYLAND

Chester Beatty Research Institute, London

MAN is exposed to natural and synthetic chemical substances which cause some mental disorders; removal or control of the causes should reduce the incidence of these disorders. For example, ergot appears to have caused mental failure in the historical past. At present, mescalin, psilocybin and lysergic acid diethylamide cause symptoms which resemble those of mental illnesses. Exposure to some industrial chemicals, such as carbon disulphide, mercury, and lead compounds, is associated with neurological and behavioural disturbances.

Some behavioural abnormalities could be caused by chemicals which are not yet recognized in the environment. If the chemicals, in the concentrations that they occur in the environment, produce detectable effects in only a few individuals, then it will be difficult to correlate these effects with their chemical causes unless some preliminary warning of the possible hazard has been given. If the effects are due to a combination of two or more factors, as is often the case with mental disease, then the causes may be even more difficult to identify.

I hope that this meeting will consider whether animal behavioural tests could and should be developed to give indications of possible hazard to mental health, mental development, or to accident proneness. Is it possible to say which tests would be appropriate? Previous Ciba Foundation symposia such as *Animal Behaviour and Drug Action* (Steinberg, de Reuck and Knight, 1964), and *Drug Responses in Man* (Wolstenholme and Porter, 1967), have considered the problems involved in the study of behavioural effects in man and animals.

A UNESCO meeting in 1968 considered that more background information on pollution was needed and "it therefore becomes necessary to bring more data from the behavioural sciences, such as psychology and sociology, into the analysis of these problems". The conclusions of this meeting included the statement: "Man's health is influenced by environmental forces. Many of his physical and mental disabilities are in large part the result of his failure to understand and to manage these often hostile forces".

It is difficult to decide on practical recommendations because of the number of environmental chemicals, estimated at 700 000, and the lack of precise criteria for differentiating between normal and abnormal behaviour in both man and animals.

Although several hundred chemical compounds of known structure cause cancer in animals, only six are known to cause cancer in both man and animals. Some procedures cause both cancer and mental disease. Irradiation of the scalp for the treatment of *Tinea tonsurans* infection increases the incidence of leukaemia, cancer and also mental illness (Albert and Omran, 1968).

Inhabitants of the island of Guam in the Far East who consume preparations of cycad meal were observed to have neurological disturbances. Rats fed on cycad meal developed cancer at many sites (Laqueur *et al.*, 1963), and a carcinogen, cycasin, was subsequently isolated from the meal. When this was fed to rats it inhibited the development of the brain and caused the rats to be less effective in solving maze problems (Haddad *et al.*, 1969). That the same material produces these different adverse effects is probably not fortuitous; some alkylating agents also produce both types of effect. These effects are examples of toxic actions like mutagenic and teratogenic effects that occur without cell death.

Although few substances are known to cause cancer in man, it is considered prudent to test food additives, drugs and other chemicals with which man comes in contact for carcinogenic activity in animals. If they are active, then they are considered as potential hazards to man. The exclusion of carcinogenic materials from the environment is one of the few known ways of reducing the incidence of cancer.

Comparative studies of behavioural changes in man and animals caused by a range of chemical substances should make it possible to be able to predict effects on human behaviour from animal experiments, although behavioural effects are variable and difficult to describe or define. Animal behavioural tests, adequate to suggest whether a particular compound might change behaviour in man, could be carried out in a few weeks. Similarly some mental or neurological effects in man might be observed within a few weeks.

There is no clear evidence of any human cancer being due to endogenous chemical factors, although hormones and trypto-phan metabolites have been suspected. Many biochemical lesions including phenylketonuria, goitres, Hartnup disease, cystathioninuria, argininosuccinicaciduria are associated with mental or neurological abnormalities. These biochemical abnormalities are inherited and although the phenotypic effects can sometimes be modified by changes of diet, the primary effects are not due to environmental influences. Similar biochemical lesions may be caused by drugs or environmental chemicals, particularly if these are antimetabolites or precursors of anti-metabolites. The occurrence of these mental diseases associated with abnormal biochemical metabolism is another reason for suspecting that some mental disease might be due to chemical factors that are not endogenous and could be avoided.

An interesting behavioural pattern associated with a bio-chemical lesion is the Lesch-Nyhan syndrome in which male subjects excrete large amounts of uric acid and bite their fingers and other parts of the body (Nyhan, 1968). Primates and the Dalmatian coachhound are the only mammals that normally excrete uric acid, but if rats are given large doses of caffeine (which is metabolized in part to methylated uric acid derivatives) they also bite their own feet. The variations in sensitivity and type of response to caffeine in man illustrate the difficulties in assessing behavioural studies.

Dogs fed bread made from flour treated with the "improver" agent, nitrogen trichloride, developed hysteria or "running fits" (Melanby, 1946). The active toxic constituent was shown to be methionine sulphoximine. The use of nitrogen trichloride in bread making was discontinued even though there was said to be no evidence that bread made from flour treated in this way had any effect on man. Methionine sulphoximine is an interesting toxic substance that inhibits the growth of some tumours in animals and has been tested as a therapeutic agent in human cancer (Krakoff, 1961). It caused mental disturbance in the patients given doses between 100 and 400 mg per day, but in one patient the mental effects were relieved by administration of methionine.

Ethionine, another carcinogenic methionine antimetabolite, also caused psychosis in five out of the six patients to whom it was given (White and Shimkin, 1954).

In 1928 the first experimental cancers were induced by a pure chemical substance, and for twenty years workers in carcinogenesis were interested in finding active carcinogens. During the last twenty years investigators have become interested in showing that compounds are not carcinogenic in animals, which indicates that they can be used without presenting a possible cancer hazard to the human population. It is generally agreed that all substances that man consumes or absorbs in other ways should be tested for carcinogenic activity before they are widely used. Most animal behaviour experiments seem to be carried out to find compounds that may be used as drugs. Is it possible to recommend that environmental chemicals, including drugs, food additives, food contaminants, and cosmetics, should be tested and shown to have no unfavourable behavioural effects in animals before they are released for wide use ?

The effects of many chemicals on behaviour are probably short lived, recovery taking place after the active compound has been removed from the body by metabolism and excretion. Some substances, however, produce permanent effects, particularly if given to young growing animals. Cycasin appears to inhibit normal brain development in rats, and hence learning ability. Irreversible damage could be of greater significance than reversible, but both types of effect need consideration.

Regulations governing the permitted or tolerated level of industrial exposure to chemicals in Eastern Europe are often based on the lowest concentrations that have an effect on behaviour (Horváth, 1961). Official international organizations, including UNESCO and WHO, have recommended that animal behavioural tests should be carried out on chemical substances with which man might come in contact.

If thousands of substances are to be so tested, then the procedure should be simple, economical and as far as possible unequivocal in its interpretation. The simpler types of behavioural studies have been discussed by Brimblecombe (1968). As biological testing is an almost universal requirement for drugs and food additives, then animals treated in 90-day toxicity tests or long-term tests could be used for behavioural studies. The length of time taken to perform chronic toxicity tests is often a serious drawback in the development of new chemicals as pesticides of food additives. If short-term behaviour tests indicated that substances were unsuitable for general use, then the time and money required for the long-term tests would be saved.

Another approach to the problem is epidemiological, by investigation of the incidence of different mental disorders in different districts and industries. This type of enquiry is likely to be the most effective in determining the causes of unusual types of disorders, especially in situations where relatively small populations can be compared.

More work is needed to relate the results of animal tests to man, and to develop new tests that would be more sensitive and significant than the existing procedures.

REFERENCES

ALBERT, R. E., and OMRAN, A. R. (1968). *Archs envir. Hlth*, **17**, 899.

BRIMBLECOMBE, R. W. (1968). In *Modern Trends in Toxicology*, pp. 149–174, ed. Boyland, E., and Goulding, R. London: Butterworths.

HADDAD, R. K., RUBE, A., LAQUEUR, G. L., SPATZ, M., and VALSAMIS, M. P. (1969). *Science*, **163**, 88.

HORVÁTH, M. (1961). In *Maximum Allowable Concentrations of Toxic Substances in Industry* (Proceedings of IUPAC International Symposium, Prague, 1959), p. 171, ed. Truhaut, R. London: Butterworths.

KRAKOFF, I. H. (1961). *Clin. Pharmac. Ther.*, **2**, 599–604.

LAQUEUR, G. L., MICKELSON, O., WHITING, M. G., and KURLAND, L. T. (1963). *J. natn. Cancer Inst.*, **31**, 919.

MELANBY, E. (1946). *Br. med. J.*, **2**, 885.

NYHAN, W. L. (1968). *Fedn Proc. Fedn Am. Socs exp. Biol.*, **27**, 1027.

STEINBERG, H., REUCK, A. V. S. de, and KNIGHT, J. (1964). *Ciba Fdn Symp. Animal Behaviour and Drug Action*. London: Churchill.

UNESCO (1968). *Intergovernmental Conference of Experts on the Scientific Basis for Rational Use and Conservation of the Resources of the Biosphere*. Paris: UNESCO.

WHITE, L. P., and SHIMKIN, M. B. (1954). *Cancer, N.Y.*, **7**, 867.

WOLSTENHOLME, G. E. W., and PORTER, R. (1967). *Ciba Fdn Symp. Drug Responses in Man*. London: Churchill.

THE USE OF ANIMAL TESTS TO PREDICT BEHAVIOURAL EFFECTS OF CHEMICALS ON MAN

R. W. Brimblecombe

Chemical Defence Establishment, Porton Down, Salisbury, Wiltshire

The pharmacologist or toxicologist is constantly confronted with the difficulty of extrapolating to man results obtained from laboratory animals. Even when drugs have well-defined modes and sites of action, differences between species often exist, usually due to variations in the manner or rate of metabolism of the compounds. With substances which modify behaviour the situation is further complicated because the neurological or biochemical substrates for specific aspects of behaviour are not understood and so the precise modes and sites of action of the substances are unknown. Consequently their pharmacological testing is essentially empirical and extrapolation to man becomes even more uncertain, particularly since some of the more subjective drug-induced effects in man may not be reproducible or recognizable in lower animals.

It is against this background of ignorance and uncertainty that the psychopharmacologist has to work. Broadly speaking he has to deal with two main groups of substances: the psychotherapeutic drugs, which tend to normalize abnormal behaviour, and the psychodysleptic drugs, which themselves produce abnormal behaviour. Reasonably satisfactory animal testing procedures are available for detecting psychotherapeutic activity, either tranquillizing or antidepressant, but less work has been carried out with psychodysleptic drugs and discussion here will be limited to that aspect of the subject.

There are three fairly well-defined groups of psychodysleptic (psychotomimetic, hallucinogenic, psychedelic, etc.) drugs. These are:

1. Sympathomimetic amines, including lysergic acid diethylamide (LSD-25), substituted tryptamines and phenylalkylamines

2. The cannabis group
3. Anticholinergic substances, including various esters of benzilic and glycolic acid

To this list should be added a fourth, miscellaneous, group containing a wide variety of chemical substances which have been reported as either regularly or occasionally producing abnormal behaviour in man. These substances can be administered deliberately in the form of drugs, or absorbed accidentally or incidentally in industrial situations or when they are used as pesticides, herbicides or food additives. Brimblecombe (1968), in a brief review, found examples of many such substances of various chemical types from a diversity of sources.

All the above types of substances produce effects which are superficially similar but which differ in detail and in the manner whereby they are produced. It is unlikely, therefore, that any single pharmacological test will reliably detect psychodysleptic activity, although the results of at least two studies suggest that such a test might be available. Corne and Pickering (1967) demonstrated that a wide selection of hallucinogenic drugs induced characteristic head-twitches in mice, an effect not produced by chemically related nonhallucinogenic compounds. Brimblecombe (1963) showed that among ten psychodysleptic drugs of varied chemical types, nine produced a decrease in emotional defaecation of rats in an open-field test. Despite these two observations it is generally agreed that it is necessary, where they are available, to use specific tests for specific types of compounds, or failing this, to employ a spectrum of tests.

Many of the available methods have been arrived at arbitrarily. Substances known to have psychodysleptic activity in man have been shown to modify, in a reproducible way, specific measurable parameters in laboratory animals. This can then form the basis of a test system for other substances of the same type. Sometimes it is possible to explain, or at least to rationalize, the use of the particular test; more often it has to be accepted empirically. The tests can be biochemical, pharmacological or purely behavioural. To illustrate their use brief accounts are given below of some methods which have been used to test for psychodysleptic activity in compounds included in Groups 1, 2, and 3 above.

1. *Sympathomimetic amines*

The use of a hyperthermic response in rabbits can predict psychodysleptic activity among indole derivatives. Hofmann (1960) showed a good parallelism between the hyperthermic potency in rabbits and the psychodysleptic potency in man of 18 derivatives of lysergic acid. Similarly, Brimblecombe (1967) showed a correlation between this hyperthermic activity of 36 tryptamine derivatives and their activity in modifying the behaviour of rats in an open-field test. The exact relevance of the latter test to human behaviour is not known but experience has shown that in compounds of this type it gives a reasonable prediction of activity in man.

A number of phenylalkylamines are also included in this group, and various testing procedures have been used for them. For example, Smythies and Sykes (1965), and Smythies, Sykes and Lord (1966) used a conditioned-avoidance response test in rats to evaluate the activity of mescaline and some of its analogues, while Fairchild and co-workers (1967) studied alterations in frequency distribution of spontaneous brain electrical activity in cats after administration of mescaline, amphetamine and certain amphetamine derivatives. The latter authors claimed that one pattern of frequency change was a correlate of the hallucinogenic effect produced in many by some of the drugs used.

2. *Cannabis group*

There are considerable differences between the various preparations of the drug cannabis, making testing difficult but, in any case, there seems to be no really satisfactory test method. Earlier workers used the development of corneal anaesthesia in rabbits or ataxia in dogs as tests of potency, but the value of these tests is very doubtful.

3. *Anticholinergic substances*

All these drugs act like atropine in that they are competitive antagonists of acetylcholine at its muscarinic sites of action in the peripheral autonomic nervous system. It has been debated whether similar antagonism of acetylcholine in the central nervous system (CNS) results in the psychodysleptic actions of these drugs. The consensus of opinion now seems to favour this view (e.g., Herz, 1963; White and Carlton, 1963) and so a measure of the central anticholinergic potencies of the drugs should indicate their psychodysleptic activity. It is only recently that drugs which appear to interact with central receptors of the muscarinic type have become available. This is the mode of action which has been suggested (Bebbington and Brimblecombe, 1965; Cox and Potkonjak, 1969) for oxotremorine, a drug which produces marked muscular tremors in various species of animals. Potency in blocking these tremors can thus be assumed to give a measure of central anticholinergic activity. Insufficient information exists about the psychodysleptic activity of these drugs in man to enable a final assessment to be made of the value of this testing procedure, although Abood (1968) gives a behavioural disturbance index (BDI) for a number of the drugs. This is an arbitrary measure of CNS activity obtained from a number of tests and Abood claims that it is a measure of psychotomimetic efficacy. Two of the compounds tested by Abood have also been tested by Brimblecombe and Green (1968) for their ability to antagonize oxotremorine-induced tremors. It is probably justifiable to add two further compounds with N-ethyl rather than N-methyl substituents, since in an earlier paper Abood and Biel (1962) imply that there is little difference between the psychodysleptic activities of compounds with these substituents. The results can then be compared (Table I).

While too much should not be read into these comparisons it seems clear that the four compounds concerned are approximately equiactive by both criteria of assessment and that the simple procedure of measuring antagonism of oxotremorine-induced tremors in mice might well give a good indication of the psychodysleptic activity of drugs of this type.

4. Miscellaneous compounds

Real testing difficulties exist among the wide variety of substances found in the environment which have no common features, either of chemical structure or biological activity, except that they produce abnormal patterns of behaviour in man and/or laboratory animals. For substances known to produce untoward behavioural effects in man it is desirable to find animal tests capable of detecting these effects so that related substances can be tested for potential hazards. On the other hand there are substances which modify the behaviour of laboratory

TABLE I

COMPARISON OF THE PSYCHODYSLEPTIC ACTIVITY OF FOUR ANTICHOLINERGIC DRUGS WITH THEIR POTENCY IN ANTAGONIZING OXOTREMORINE-INDUCED TREMORS IN MICE

Compound	Behavioural disturbance index	ED_{50} (μmol/kg with 95% limits) for antagonism of oxotremorine-induced tremors in mice[‡]

R	R'		
CH_3	(phenyl)	12·8[*]	1·8 (1·0–3·2)
C_2H_5	(phenyl)	12·8[†]	2·7 (1·4–5·3)
CH_3	(cyclopentyl)	13·2[*]	2·0 (1·5–2·7)
C_2H_5	(cyclopentyl)	13·2[†]	3·1 (1·8–5·3)

[*] Quoted by Abood, 1968.
[†] Assumed.
[‡] From Brimblecombe and Green, 1968.

animals and it is necessary to determine whether the modifications which occur are of any significance in terms of human behaviour.

There are examples in the literature of animal studies being carried out following reports of compounds producing mental effects in man. Thus, Ahlmark and Forssman (1951), and Grandjean and co-workers (1955) reported nervous system disturbances in workers exposed to the industrial solvent trichloroethylene. Subsequently, various workers (e.g. Formánek and Horváth, 1957; Grandjean, 1960) demonstrated effects of this compound on animal behaviour.

It is of relevance to compare the animal and human studies on this substance. Formánek and Horváth (1957) found that in conditioned rats concentrations of 75 p.p.m. produced a decrease in the latency of response, an increase in inter-trial motor activity, and disorders in discrimination. Much higher concentrations (2500–5500 p.p.m.) were required to increase the latency of response and finally to block completely conditioned responses. Grandjean (1960) used concentrations between 200 and 800 p.p.m. for periods of three hours and found no effect on conditioned responses of rats in a rope-climbing test, but the animals showed increased numbers of spontaneous climbs, an effect interpreted by the author as indicating a modification in the psychological equilibrium of the rats with reduction in inhibition or increase in excitation.

Recently Vernon and Ferguson (1969) have studied the effects of trichloroethylene on human visual-motor performance. Concentrations of 100, 300 and 1000 p.p.m. were breathed for periods of two hours; only the latter concentration had any effect on visual perception or motor skill.

Allowing for the variation in experimental conditions there is fair agreement between the animal and human studies. Taken together they seem to confirm that the standard laid down for trichloroethylene by the U.S. Standards Institute (maximum concentrations of 300 p.p.m. should not be inhaled for more than 5 min in any 2 h period) is reasonable and that the results of animal behavioural tests with this substance can be extrapolated to man with some confidence.

Methyl Cellosolve is another industrial solvent which has been reported to produce transient changes in the behaviour and personality of workers exposed to it. Goldberg, Haun and Smyth (1962) exposed rats to concentrations of 500 p.p.m. of this substance for two weeks, and found that these animals failed to acquire a conditioned avoidance response. Slightly higher concentrations blocked an already established response. There were no overt signs of poisoning in these animals, but in contrast ethanol only affected conditioned responses at a concentration of 3200 p.p.m. when the animals were ataxic. A distinction was thus made between the specific effects of methyl cellosolve and the non-specific effects of ethanol. Subsequently Goldberg and co-workers (1964) carried out similar studies with other industrial

solvents and found that five of them showed specific effects
similar to those of Methyl Cellosolve. At least two of these
solvents, trichloroethylene and carbon disulphide, have been
reported to produce behavioural changes in man. A solvent,
perchloroethylene, said by Goldberg and co-workers to show
non-specific effects like those of ethanol, is reported by Patty
(1962) to produce sleepiness and lightheadedness in man only at
concentrations which also produce motor incoordination. This
indicates a similarity between the human response and that found
in laboratory animals.

There are many compounds which modify the behaviour of
laboratory animals at doses which have produced no well-
documented effects in man. Examples will be taken from the
field of cholinesterase inhibitors, a class of compounds used as
insecticides, and so present, at least in some areas of the world,
in the environment.

Animal behavioural studies with cholinesterase inhibitors of the
organophosphorus type have indicated that changes are only
detectable in animals with considerable reductions in brain
cholinesterase activity. Russell, Watson and Frankenhauser
(1961) used Systox (O,O-diethyl S-ethylmercaptoethyl thio-
phosphate) and showed that it increased the rate of extinction
of a conditioned response in rats, but only when there was a
60 to 65 per cent reduction in brain cholinesterase activity.
The blood cholinesterase levels in these animals must also have
been considerably reduced. Similarly Pan'shina (1963) found that
40 mg/kg of the organophosphorus insecticide, phosphamide,
modified conditioned responses in a cat without producing any
overt signs of poisoning. Serum and erythrocyte cholinesterase
levels were reduced by 40 per cent or more. The author, in
unpublished experiments with other organophosphates, has only
been able to detect behavioural changes in rats using $0.2 \times LD_{50}$
doses which produce considerable depletion in blood cholinesterase levels.

Such results suggest that any behavioural effects of compounds
of this type will occur only after absorption of doses which produce measurable depression of blood cholinesterase. However,
recent studies have shown that some cholinesterase inhibitors
produce behavioural effects apparently unrelated to their enzyme-
inhibiting activity.

TABLE II

LIST OF COMPOUNDS WITH THEIR ACTIVITIES IN INHIBITING CHOLINESTERASES *in vitro*, THEIR TOXICITIES AND THEIR ACTIVITIES IN THE OPEN-FIELD TEST

General formula
$$\begin{array}{c} R' \\ R \end{array}\!\!>\!\!P\!=\!O \atop R''$$

Compound number	R	R'	R''	K_{OH^-} ($l.mol^{-1}min^{-1}$)	AChE K_{in} ($l.mol^{-1}min^{-1}$) Bovine erythrocyte	AChE K_{in} ($l.mol^{-1}min^{-1}$) Rat brain	Pseudo-ChE K_{in} ($l.mol^{-1}min^{-1}$)	LD_{50} (mg/kg) s.c. rats	Approx M.E.D. open-field test (mg/kg) s.c. rats	Ratio LD_{50}/M.E.D.
1	CH_3	$ClCH_2CH_2O$	$Cl_2C=CHO$	$3\cdot2\times10^3$	7×10^3	$4\cdot7\times10^3$	$2\cdot3\times10^3$	0·79	0·1	8
2	C_2H_5	$ClCH_2CH_2O$	$Cl_2C=CHO$	$9\cdot0\times10^1$	$3\cdot7\times10^3$	$4\cdot2\times10^3$	$3\cdot1\times10^5$	1·25	0·02	62
3	CH_3	FCH_2CH_2O	$Cl_2C=CHO$	$2\cdot1\times10^1$	$4\cdot6\times10^3$	$3\cdot2\times10^5$	$1\cdot5\times10^5$	2·69	0·1	27
4	CH_3	C_2H_5O	$Cl_2C=CHO$	$1\cdot6\times10^2$	$1\cdot2\times10^3$	3×10^3	4×10^4	1·01	0·1	10
5	CH_3	C_2H_5O	$ClCH_2CH_2O$	0·35	$6\cdot9\times10^1$	$7\cdot5\times10^1$	$2\cdot8\times10^2$	>50	0·01	>5000
6	C_2H_5O	C_2H_5O	$Cl_2C=CHO$	2·5	$1\cdot3\times10^2$	2×10^2	$3\cdot5\times10^5$	15·5	0·2	77
7	C_2H_5O	C_2H_5O	$ClCH_2CH_2O$	1·0	$1\cdot0\times10^2$	8×10^1	$5\cdot6\times10^4$	13·0	5	3
8	CH_3O	CH_3O	$Cl_2C=CHO$	$4\cdot0\times10^1$	$1\cdot3\times10^2$	3×10^2	$3\cdot4\times10^4$	35	0·2	175

Some halogen-containing phosphorus esters were studied for their ability to inhibit acetylcholinesterase and cholinesterase *in vitro* and *in vivo* and for their activity in modifying the open-field behaviour of rats. The results are summarized in Tables II and III.

TABLE III

INHIBITION OF RAT BLOOD AND BRAIN CHOLINESTERASE *in vivo* BY SOME OF THE ESTERS. BLOOD AND BRAIN SAMPLES TAKEN AT 90 MIN AFTER INJECTION, OR AT DEATH WHEN THIS OCCURRED EARLIER. ALL VALUES REPRESENT THE MEAN OF EIGHT ESTIMATIONS

Compound number	Dose mg/kg (subcutaneously)	Brain	Plasma	Erythrocytes	Remarks
1	0·05	1	0	12	
	0·1	0	17	31	
	0·2	5	42	62	
	0·4	31	50	73	
4	0·05	0	25	24	
	0·1	0	24	31	
	0·2	9	55	66	
	0·4	39	78	88	
2	0·003	1	0	0	
	0·02	2	8	0	
	0·12	5	15	23	
	0·72	58	79	86	⅜ rats died
6	0·125	0	7	2	
	0·5	20	31	24	
	2·0	72	67	71	
	8·0	88	88	92	All rats died
5	400	2	0	(whole blood)	

Column header: % inhibition of cholinesterase (spans Brain, Plasma, Erythrocytes).

The esters inhibited all the cholinesterase preparations used. Statistically significant correlations were found between rates of enzyme inhibition (log k_{In}) and the rates at which hydroxyl ions catalysed the hydrolysis of the phosphorus esters (log $k_{OH}-$). This suggests that the rate-controlling step in both the inhibitory and the hydrolytic processes is the same, presumably P–X bond fission. Significant correlations were also found between log k_{In} values and log LD_{50}s suggesting that the lethality of the esters was due to their anticholinesterase activity. No correlation, however, existed between log k_{In} values and activities in modifying open-field behaviour and, in addition, the latter effect occurred in rats in which brain cholinesterase levels were virtually un-affected.

It is possible that significant depletions in brain cholinesterase levels were present in specific areas of the brain but were not detected by this method which simply measured levels in whole-brain homogenates, but it is tempting to speculate that the phos-phate esters produced their behavioural effects by some means other than inhibition of brain cholinesterase. With some of the compounds there was a 20 to 30 per cent inhibition of blood cholinesterase in rats given doses equivalent to minimal effective open-field doses. Clearly this is not a reliable index for predicting these behavioural effects, neither is inhibition of cholinesterase in peripheral tissues likely to be responsible for them since experi-ence in our laboratory with other cholinesterase inhibitors has shown that open-field behaviour of rats is not affected until blood cholinesterase levels are depleted by more than 70 per cent.

These behavioural effects were transient; animals tested at three, rather than one and a half hours after administration were unaffected. The effects were obscure and apparently specific to this test since subsequent studies using other test systems and other species have not produced similar results. Nevertheless this illustrates a familiar kind of dilemma. The results can be dismissed as being of no relevance to man until evidence is pro-vided to suggest otherwise, or they can be taken as indicating that the compounds concerned are potentially dangerous to man at the kind of dose levels used. There is no simple solution. Ideally, carefully controlled experiments on man should be carried out to obtain information about the possible behavioural effects of the compounds. In practice, however, the only information that is likely to be forthcoming is from accidental exposures to the compounds, should any of them be used industrially.

In conclusion it can be stated that simple and reasonably satisfactory animal tests exist for some classes of psychodysleptic drugs, but it is still difficult to test individual substances. At pres-ent, animal behavioural studies are most suitable for screening purposes, but whenever possible it is desirable to develop relevant biochemical or pharmacological techniques which are easier to carry out and which, in general, give more reproducible results. The greatest handicap to further development in this area is the lack of precise data on the effects on human behaviour of many substances present in the environment. Only when such data are available for correlation with the results of animal tests will much progress be made.

SUMMARY

Compounds which modify behaviour act on little-understood neurological or biochemical substrates and so present particularly great difficulties in extrapolation to man of results obtained with laboratory animals. Nevertheless, for the sympathomimetic and anticholinergic groups of psychodysleptic drugs, animal test methods are now available which seem to give reliable estimates of activity in man. In each case simple pharmacological techniques, rather than complicated behavioural methods, can be used.

Behavioural methods must, however, be used for screening potential psychodysleptic substances with no clear-cut biochemical or pharmacological actions which seem relevant to their psycho-dysleptic activity. Where human data are available the requirement is to find a specific technique which will give reliable information about the behavioural effects of a substance and its close relatives. This has been achieved in various instances. In the absence of human data it is extremely difficult to assess the significance in man of compounds which influence the behaviour of laboratory animals. At the present state of knowledge evaluation of such results must await controlled human trials or, more commonly, accidental exposures in man.

Acknowledgements

Some of the experiments reported here were carried out in collaboration with Mr D. B. Coult, Mr C. C. Deane, and Mr D. C. Parkes.

REFERENCES

ABOOD, L. G. (1968). In *Drugs Affecting the Central Nervous System*, pp. 127–167, ed. Burger, A. New York: Dekker.

ABOOD, L. G., and BIEL, J. H. (1962). *Int. Rev. Neurobiol.*, **4**, 217–273.

AHLMARK, A., and FORSSMAN, S. (1951). *Archs ind. Hyg.*, **3**, 386–398.

BEBBINGTON, A., and BRIMBLECOMBE, R. W. (1965). *Adv. Drug Res.*, **2**, 143–172.

BRIMBLECOMBE, R. W. (1963). *Psychopharmacologia*, **4**, 139–147.

BRIMBLECOMBE, R. W. (1967). *Int. J. Neuropharmac.*, **6**, 423–429.

BRIMBLECOMBE, R. W. (1968). In *Modern Trends in Toxicology*, pp. 149–174, ed. Boyland, E., and Goulding, R. London: Butterworths.

BRIMBLECOMBE, R. W., and GREEN, D. M. (1968). *Int. J. Neuropharmac.*, **7**, 15–21.

CORNE, S. J., and PICKERING, R. W. (1967). *Psychopharmacologia*, **11**, 65–78.

COX, B., and POTKONJAK, D. (1969). *Br. J. Pharmac.*, **35**, 521–529.

FAIRCHILD, M. D., ALLES, G. A., JENDEN, D. J., and MICKEY, M. R. (1967). *Int. J. Neuropharmac.*, **6**, 151–167.

FORMÁNEK, J., and HORVÁTH, M. (1957). *Pracovní Lék*, **9**, 39.

GOLDBERG, M. E., HAUN, C., and SMYTH, H. F. (1962). *Toxic. appl. Pharmac.*, **4**, 148–164.

GOLDBERG, M. E., JOHNSON, H. E., POZZANI, U. C., and SMYTH, H. F. (1964). *Am. ind. Hyg. Ass. J.*, **25**, 369–375.

GRANDJEAN, E. (1960). *Archs envir. Hlth*, **1**, 106–108.

GRANDJEAN, E., MÜNCHINGER, R., TURRIAN, V., HASS, P. A., KNOEPFEL, H. K., and ROSENMUND, H. (1955). *Br. J. ind. Med.*, **12**, 131–140.

HERZ, A. (1963). *Int. J. Neuropharmac.*, **2**, 205–216.

HOFMANN, A. (1960). *Svensk kem. Tidskr.*, **72**, 723–747.

PAN'SHINA, T. N. (1963). *Bull. exp. Biol. Med. U.S.S.R.*, **56**, 1347–1350.

PATTY, F. A. (ed.) (1962). *Industrial Hygiene and Toxicology*. New York: Wiley Interscience.

RUSSELL, R. W., WATSON, R. H. J., and FRANKENHAUSER, M. (1961). *Scand. J. Psychol.*, **2**, 21–29.

SMYTHIES, J. R., and SYKES, E. A. (1965). *Psychopharmacologia*, **8**, 324–330.

SMYTHIES, J. R., SYKES, E. A., and LORD, C. P. (1966). *Psychopharmacologia*, **9**, 434–446.

VERNON, R. J., and FERGUSON, R. K. (1969). *Archs envir. Hlth*, **18**, 894–900.

WHITE, R. P., and CARLTON, R. A. (1963). *Psychopharmacologia*, **4**, 459–471.

DISCUSSION

Boyland: Do you consider that Hall's open-field test is too simple to enable one to make predictions about behaviour in man?

Brimblecombe: Yes, the results are difficult to interpret. However, there are people who take the view that a dose of a substance producing any effect, be it behavioural, pathological or of any other kind, should be considered hazardous.

Harris: What is an open-field test?

Brimblecombe: The open-field is a circular drum which is divided into sections. This novel situation evokes in a naive rat a rather stereotyped pattern of behaviour, various aspects of which are scored. This basic pattern is modified in different ways by different types of centrally acting drugs. A difficulty with the organophosphorus cholinesterase inhibitors, the drugs that I referred to, was that they did not all modify behaviour in the same way, which makes it even more difficult to explain or understand the results.

Boyland: One difficulty with behavioural tests is that behaviour might either improve or deteriorate as a result of treatment.

Brimblecombe: Yes, but we have looked at these compounds in other test situations and there is no evidence for increment in performance.

Philp: I think you are quite right, Dr Brimblecombe, when you say that once you have an effect in one type of test, people tend to assume that you have really shown something and hold you to it, irrespective of whether you yourself can interpret it as being harmful or beneficial. It is preferable, therefore, to be sure of the relevance of any particular test before including it in a programme of tests for particular chemicals. With these anticholinesterase compounds did you find any tie-up with other behavioural tests?

Brimblecombe: We have not been able to affect behaviour in any other test situation with these compounds at these doses; higher doses are needed to do this.

Philp: Have you a hypothesis as to what the open-field behaviour depends on?

Brimblecombe: It is possible to rationalize the actions of some drugs on open-field behaviour in terms of their effects on an emotional response, but there is no reasonable explanation for the actions of these anticholinesterase compounds.

Albert: What is the mechanism of production of the hyperthermia?

Brimblecombe: This effect is central in origin. Neuhold, Taeschler and Cerletti (1957) showed that in decorticated rabbits lysergic acid diethylamide (LSD-25) still had a hyperthermic effect, but this effect was absent after removal of the cerebrum and midbrain or after decerebration. It was concluded that the probable site of action was the diencephalon. With LSD-25, and probably other tryptamine derivatives, the effects on behaviour and the hyperthermia are probably both manifestations of central nervous system excitation.

Harris: Does your temperature go up when you take LSD?

Brimblecombe: I know of no specific evidence for this; the rabbit is particularly sensitive, as it is to all pyrogens.

Marley: I should like to make one caveat about temperature and sympathomimetic amines: quite opposite effects on temperature may be obtained with the same amine in the same species. These differences in effect appear to depend on the temperature difference between body and environment. For example, in a species in which catecholamines usually lower temperature, if environmental temperature is raised thereby reducing the temperature difference between body and environment, the same dose of catecholamine may now raise body temperature. Conversely, should environmental temperature fall below thermoneutrality the hyperthermic effects of the catecholamine are enhanced. Consequently, drug effects on temperature can have little meaning unless they are related to standard situations and to the particular ambient temperature.

Brimblecombe: We do our experiments in a reasonably well-thermoregulated room, but take no other precautions.

Steinberg: Banks and Russell (1967) worked on Systox, which is an anticholinesterase. They used the Hebb–Williams test, which can be regarded as an amalgam of an open-field and of a learning test, and it can be arranged so as to include problems of increasing difficulty. I believe they found this test method fairly sensitive.

Brimblecombe: This insecticide is referred to in my paper. Using Systox, effects were only found when brain cholinesterase was depleted by 60 per cent or more.

Steinberg: Have you considered using the Hebb-Williams test as a test for your compound?

Brimblecombe: No, but it might be useful.

Joyce: I thought you said effects on behaviour in the open-field test are detectable at smaller doses than those needed to affect cholinesterases. If so, this worries me.

Brimblecombe: It would worry me much more if behavioural changes could be shown with similar doses, in rats or in other species, in other test situations, or if the effects were long-lasting or permanent. Is the fact that we have only been able to show effects in this one particular test necessarily worrying?

Weiskrantz: It depends on the question you are asking. If you are only interested in screening, then obviously you try to find a test that is sensitive to any compound. But I do not think you have legitimate grounds to stop worrying until you have determined what the effect is by more analytical testing.

Joyce: The very name "open-field test" seems to suggest a degree of generality that may not be really appropriate.

Weiskrantz: Yes. The ideal screening test is presumably one which has so many different aspects of behaviour combined in it that one is likely to pick up at least something. The difficulty is that the question about screening is antithetical to the question about mechanism. The screening test is the crude instrument that allows you to get to work. But if you do not go beyond the crude instrument you have no right to become easy about the situation.

Brimblecombe: I suppose the open-field should be regarded as a crude instrument. We have gone on to other tests which are more refined and we have not found behavioural effects.

King: When you put an animal into an open-field for the first time it does not move around freely, but stays close to the walls (Brimblecombe, 1963; Phillips and Bradley, 1969). With the exception of this behaviour and complete immobility, all other responses have a low frequency. For this reason one might expect an open-field test to be more sensitive to an incapacitating drug than most operant conditioning situations where responses having a high probability of occurrence are being measured. Chlorpromazine, for example, has been shown to reduce ambulation at doses of 0·5 mg/kg (Ryall, 1958; Phillips and Bradley, 1969), whereas doses in excess of 1·5 mg/kg must be given before an animal fails to escape from shock (Heise and Boff, 1962; Morpurgo, 1965).

Boyland: Is it possible to say whether these low levels of anticholinesterase compounds affect human subjects?

Barnes: A series of tests in the United States has shown no evidence that mental alertness is affected in men exposed to organophosphorus insecticides. The study was primarily directed at discovering a possible cause of accidents to aircraft when spraying crops. Mental alertness was only affected in people with clinical symptoms of poisoning (Durham, Wolfe and Quinby, 1965). Performance can be affected by a splash of an anticholinesterase in one eye only, with unilateral effects on accommodation.

Steinberg: Why are all these compounds classified as psychodysleptic, which as far as I know means something like "tearing the psyche apart"? I think the importance of doses should be very strongly underlined and also the importance of the circumstances in which they are given; for something that may tear the psyche apart in one dose may pull it together in another, and the same is true of circumstances.

Brimblecombe: I hold no particular brief for this term. I thought it was the best one available.

Joyce: One traditional term is "Phantastica", or phantasticants (Lewin, 1931).

Kety: Perhaps psychodysleptic implies too much in terms of the behaviour that you noted. It would be difficult to demonstrate a psychodysleptic effect in animals.

Marley: Dr Steinberg, would you say that, in general, non-learned behaviours are probably more susceptible to modification by drugs than learned behaviours?

Steinberg: Yes, because behaviour which has not become fixed by repetition or training is apt to be more labile and hence more easily influenced.

Marley: So one should first watch for effects on non-learned behaviours.

Steinberg: In so far as any behaviour is non-learned.

Marley: If the effects of sympathomimetic amines are compared over a dose range in the same species, modification of non-learned behaviours is obtained with smaller doses than are required for altering learned (operant) behaviour. This suggests that the latter is extremely stable and less easy to modify by drugs. It may be that the sensitivity of the two types of behaviour overlap and I happened to be comparing a non-learned behaviour which was extremely sensitive to drugs with a learned behaviour that was rather insensitive.

Cowley: Dr Brimblecombe, my impression is that when one administers these drugs one produces a change either in metabolism or in the actual food intake of the animal. Could there be a common element in many of these situations, so that it is the alteration in nutrition rather than the drug that produces the behavioural changes? I am assuming that when you use the open-field test you use the usual intense light plus some sort of background noise. These are essential features of the test, and behaviour is quite different without them.

Brimblecombe: We use bright light and a white noise generator.

Cowley: Is there a change of food intake?

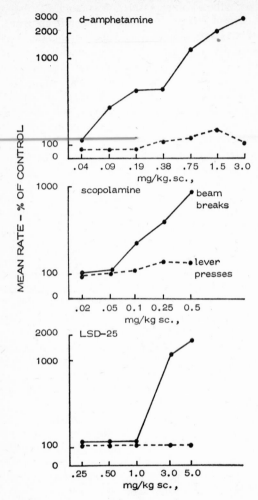

Fig. 1 (*King*). Interactions between shock-avoidance rate and locomotor activity (G. A. Heise and E. Boff, 1970, unpublished).

Brimblecombe: This has not been measured, but I do not think it is relevant as the whole experiment only lasts for three hours.

King: George Heise sent me some data from work on the effects of LSD-25, scopolamine and amphetamine (Fig. 1). He obtained dose response relationships, measuring conditioned avoidance in a lever-pressing situation. At the same time he put photo-electric cells across the Skinner boxes and measured the amount of motor activity. He found that the lever-pressing response was relatively insensitive, but with all three drugs the beam breaks showed an increase in frequency. This is one of the problems with operant situations; behaviour is only being sampled part of the time.

Steinberg: This is consistent with what I said earlier: labile behaviour is liable to be more sensitive than anything that is too fixed.

Silverman: But it might also be too sensitive to accidental environmental influences that you are not testing. In the ideal test, what you measure is stable when you do not do anything, but labile when you do.

Steinberg: Yes; for many purposes it is helpful to have a delicate balance between a stable baseline and responsiveness to drugs and other stimuli.

Joyce: If the attention of a subject is focused on one particular measure of his behaviour that is under modification by drugs or other means, he is able to control it, or to compensate to such an extent that no changes are detectable. Whereas if a number of detecting instruments and dummy leads are attached to him so that he no longer knows what is being observed, changes can be detected.

Lewis: Dr Brimblecombe, do you have any data on the effect of alcohol in your experimental situation?

Brimblecombe: We have only given large doses which were clearly depressant.

Lewis: The effect might be related to dosage.

Brimblecombe: Yes, I agree.

REFERENCES

BANKS, A., and RUSSELL, R. W. (1967). *J. comp. physiol. Psychol.*, **64**, 161.
BRIMBLECOMBE, R. W. (1963). *Psychopharmacologia*, **4**, 139–147.

Durham, W. F., Wolfe, H. R., and Quinby, G. E. (1965). *Archs envir. Hlth,* **10,** 55–66.

Heise, G. A., and Boff, E. (1962). *Psychopharmacologia,* **3,** 264–282.

Lewin, L. (1931). *Phantastica: Narcotic and Stimulating Drugs.* London: Routledge and Kegan Paul.

Morpurgo, C. (1965). *Psychopharmacologia,* **8,** 91–99.

Neuhold, K., Taeschler, M., and Cerletti, A. (1957). *Helv. physiol. pharmac. Acta,* **15,** 1–7.

Phillips, M. I., and Bradley, P. B. (1969). *Int. J. Neuropharmac.,* **8,** 167–176.

Ryall, R. W. (1958). *Nature, Lond.,* **182,** 1606–1607.

A LABORATORY MODEL FOR BEHAVIOUR AS AN INDICATOR OF TOXICITY

A. P. SILVERMAN

Industrial Hygiene Research Laboratories, ICI Limited, Alderley Park

IN toxicology it is usually important to estimate a threshold dose below which a chemical is not likely to have any harmful effects. This is often as important as it is to describe the harmful effects of higher doses, but it raises difficulties. Not only must the most sensitive method be found, but agreement must be reached about the interpretation of the results. What is "harmful" and how far animal results can be extrapolated to man is in the last resort a personal decision (but see Boissier and Simon, 1967). In this paper I would like to discuss the claim (e.g. Medved, Spynu and Kagan, 1964) that behavioural tests can be the most sensitive indicators of toxicity.

Any compound, in a large enough dose, is likely to be "toxic" to laboratory animals. But although their behaviour may be altered, there could be so much else wrong with the animals that the behavioural change is not very interesting. The claim that behaviour is especially sensitive probably arose because a few chemicals, like so-called psychotropic drugs, have behavioural effects that may be loosely described as specific. This is not to say that they have no other actions, since a behavioural effect necessarily depends on a neurophysiological action, and this in turn depends on a molecular action. But it means that the behavioural change is measurable at doses where the underlying physiological and biochemical effects are difficult to detect with available methods, or where their significance is even harder to interpret than the behavioural aspect.

Nicotine is a good example because it is the principal active constituent of tobacco smoke (Hall, 1970), which many people inhale presumably for its psychological effects; although nicotine has other properties which have made it a useful tool in many aspects of physiology. A number of behavioural effects ascribed to nicotine have been described in animals; changes in wheel-running, in learning conditioned-avoidance tasks, and in several operant schedules with a water reward (Bovet, Bovet-Nitti and Oliverio, 1967; Domino, 1967; Armitage, Hall and Morrison, 1968). It is interesting that the type of effect depends to some extent on the dose, the situation, and the individual animals. The smallest effective dose in these experiments was 50 μg/kg, injected intravenously. Rats have been trained to press a lever causing them to receive an intravenous injection of about 5 μg/kg of nicotine, and they take a total of about 250 μg/kg in one session (Clark, 1969). On a physiological level, Hall (1970) observed effects on the electrocorticogram of *encéphale isolé* cats during intravenous injections of 2 μg/kg of nicotine every 30 seconds. These caused a steady change in cortical activity; typical effects were obtained after about 14 μg/kg and maximal effects after 15 to 20 injections, that is after at least 30 μg/kg had been given. Ginzel (1967), and Hoff and Hockman (1967) found that the cardiac and pressor effects varied when doses in the range one to 100 μg/kg were administered under various conditions. Armitage, Hall and Morrison (1968) estimated that a man smoking a cigarette inhales a dose of nicotine approximately equivalent to 15 to 30 μg/kg intravenously.

I have observed the social behaviour of male laboratory rats given a subcutaneous dose of 25 μg/kg of nicotine (Silverman, 1970). Sixteen hooded rats and 16 albinos were housed in pairs, each pair containing one albino and one hooded, randomly allocated. Each pair was separated for five to six hours every weekday, and observed at weekly intervals for a six-minute period after they were reunited. After a few days of this routine the rats show considerable activity, and an observer, tape-recording the acts and postures described by Grant and Mackintosh (1963), can obtain what is apparently a fairly complete description of the behaviour of a rat. These behavioural elements can be grouped into a number of functional categories which are easier to analyse statistically. I hope to show that the behaviour revealed in this way is fairly stable and yet remains sensitive to several distinct drug effects.

The design of the experiment is illustrated in Fig. 1. Sixteen rats of each strain were randomly allocated to the treatment groups, eight to the experimental group and eight to the control group. (In five cages both rats of the pair received the experimental treatment; in five both received the control treatment,

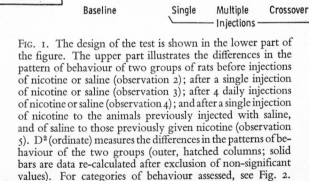

Significance levels
before rejection
(open bar) (df = 8,23)

D^2

8 —

$p < .001$ — 6

$p < .01$ — 4

$p < .05$ —
$p < .1$ - - - 2

0
Observation   2   3   4   5

saline

nicotine

Baseline   Single   Multiple   Crossover
                └──────── Injections ────────┘

FIG. 1. The design of the test is shown in the lower part of
the figure. The upper part illustrates the differences in the
pattern of behaviour of two groups of rats before injections
of nicotine or saline (observation 2); after a single injection
of nicotine or saline (observation 3); after 4 daily injections
of nicotine or saline (observation 4); and after a single injection
of nicotine to the animals previously injected with saline,
and of saline to those previously given nicotine (observation
5). D^2 (ordinate) measures the differences in the patterns of behaviour of the two groups (outer, hatched columns; solid
bars are data re-calculated after exclusion of non-significant
values). For categories of behaviour assessed, see Fig. 2.

saline injections; and in six cages one rat was experimental
and one was a control.)

The first observation was a "warm-up" test, and is not
illustrated in Fig. 1. Observation 2 was a baseline comparison
of the behaviour of the two treatment groups into which the rats
of each strain had been allocated. A multivariate test (Discriminant Analysis, Rao, 1952) showed a just significant difference
($P \approx 0.05$) in the pattern of behaviour of the two groups. A week
later, immediately before observation 3, one group of animals
received a single injection of 25 µg/kg of nicotine subcutaneously
and the control group received an injection of saline, and the
difference (observation 3) between the groups was twice as great
($P < 0.01$) as in the baseline test. The difference in behaviour of
the two groups was greater still ($P < 0.001$) after the last of four
daily injections of nicotine to one group and saline to the control
group, but when the former control rats received nicotine and
the rats which had previously received nicotine now received
saline, the difference between the groups was reduced to insignifi-
cance. There seems to be a stable difference between randomly
allocated untreated groups of rats, and the behavioural effect of
nicotine seems to be additive to this and of similar magnitude.

The computer programme for the Discriminant Analysis has a
refinement by which behavioural categories can be rejected
if their contribution to the overall difference in pattern is not
significant. The remaining contributions are recalculated, and
can therefore be used to show which kinds of behaviour have been
significantly affected.

Fig. 2 shows the contributions of each category to the differences
between the experimental and control groups of animals. The
effects of the drug are shown even more clearly within groups of
animals, by comparing the behaviour of rats when they were
injected with nicotine with when they received saline. On either
comparison (between groups or within groups), the behaviour
mainly affected by nicotine was aggression. This was significantly
less in the group that subsequently received nicotine than in the
second, the subsequent control group, in the baseline observation,
and was very much less after one or several injections of nicotine.
However in the "cross-over" observation, when they now received saline, the "experimental" group was more aggressive
than the ex-controls which had previously received saline and

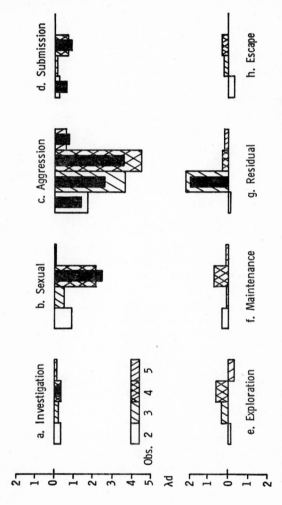

FIG. 2. Contributions of eight types of behaviour to the differences in overall behavioural pattern between the two groups of rats in observations 2–5 in Fig. 1. Behavioural categories significantly affected by nicotine are shown by the inner solid bars of the histograms (re-calculated after rejection of non-significant contributions).

were now injected with nicotine (Fig. 2). A regression equation was computed and showed that strain and group differences and injection with saline or nicotine account quite reasonably for the percentage of aggression observed (see Fig. 3).

The total numbers of behavioural elements recorded (the "activity") was not significantly affected by nicotine, so a general "arousal" effect was not very likely. Fig. 2 shows that other approach-behaviours (investigation, sexual behaviour, and submission) were only affected after the multiple injections, and then only slightly. Behaviour not oriented to the other rat of the pair (exploration and maintenance) was unaffected. The reduction in aggression was not secondary to any increase in escape from the other rat. After the initial nicotine injection it could have been secondary to the increases in the residual category which includes signs of what Lim and Guzman (1968) call the rat's equivalent of nausea, but this would not account for the continued reduction in aggression in the latter observations when residual behaviour was not increased. So this reduction in aggression was probably fairly specific.

The precise nature of the effect of nicotine is interesting in its own right, although there is some evidence that both in man and animals it depends considerably on the situation. For the present purposes what matters is that a drug, taken by man for what must be described as its psychological effects, has been shown to have effects by a particular test in rats at a comparable and very low dose. It seems a reasonable claim, therefore, that if some other substance alters the social behaviour of rats, then the possible effects of that substance in man become relevant. Such effects may or may not be of toxicological importance: the effect of nicotine was similar in magnitude and kind to the pre-existing differences between rats, so that a behavioural action like that of nicotine is not very likely to be harmful in itself. Of course the effect of a chemical on human behaviour may not be the same as that in rats—but it probably exists.

Nevertheless, it is likely that most chemicals have no particular behavioural effects at low doses, and the effects they do have at higher doses are secondary to such things as pain, or respiratory congestion. Methylene bis thiocyanate, which is used as a bactericide, may be an example of this. Twenty-four male rats were paired off, one albino being housed with one hooded rat, as in the nicotine experiments, and were randomly allocated to two groups.

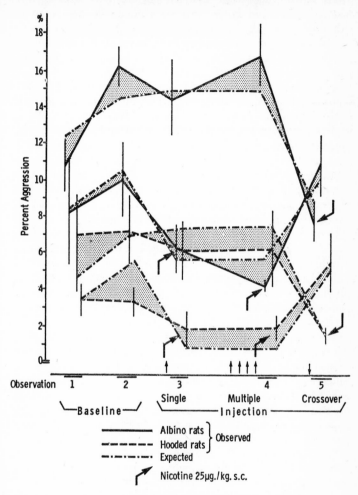

FIG. 3. Means and standard errors (vertical lines) of aggressive behaviour as a percentage of total activity, compared with percentage of aggression expected from the regression equation, before and after injections of nicotine (25 μg/kg, subcutaneously) to hooded and albino rats. Four groups each of eight rats.

There was no significant difference between the groups in a baseline observation, nor was there when one group had received a dose of 0·5 mg/kg methylene bis thiocyanate intraperitoneally about 20 minutes earlier. However, when the second group received a dose of 1 mg/kg its behaviour differed both from its own previous behaviour after a control injection of saline ($P<0·02$) and from that of the first group, now given saline ("cross-over" design) ($P<0·01$). The difference was mainly in the residual category of behaviour, notably an increase in head-raising and abdominal contractions, which are both probably signs of pain or discomfort; the rats also tended to groom the site of injection. These actions are consistent with the known local irritant action of this compound. The total activity of the rats was also reduced ($P<0·01$ by analysis of variance), by 20 per cent after the larger dose. This is also what would be expected if pain or anything else were to inhibit behaviour in general.

In the last resort, experiments with animals can only be guides to the safe limits for human exposure; but behavioural tests can provide useful comparisons with conventional toxicology even when the behavioural effects are not very clear-cut. For example, vinyl acetate is used on a large scale in the production of emulsion paints, gramophone records, etc. The problem arose of setting a Threshold Limit Value (TLV) for the maximum concentration of the vapour to which workmen could be safely exposed as an average for an eight-hour working day. The vapour has an irritant action on the eyes, nose and lungs of rats, which could be observed at concentrations above 100 to 250 p.p.m. (Gage, 1967). and a tentative TLV of 50 p.p.m. was therefore proposed. Gofmekler (1960) stated that the human sensory threshold could be as low as 0·5 p.p.m., and that reflex changes in the EEG could be found at still lower concentrations.

The social behaviour of groups of eight rats was observed immediately after exposure to vinyl acetate for five to six hours a day and compared to that of groups of eight controls (Silverman, 1967). Fig. 4 shows that there was an effect on the pattern of behaviour, significant at the five per cent level, only after exposure for three days to 500 p.p.m. of vinyl acetate. Exposure to lower concentrations did not cause significant changes in behaviour, although one of the two tests at 50 p.p.m. approached significance after 14 days.

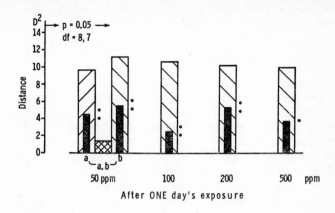

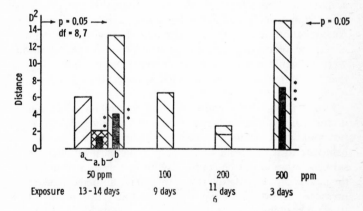

FIG. 4. Differences (D^2; hatched columns) in patterns of behaviour between two randomly allocated groups of eight rats after exposure to vinyl acetate vapour for 5 to 6 hours per day for periods from 1 to 11 days. Two tests, *a* and *b*, were done at 50 p.p.m. and *a·b* shows the combined results. Three observations were made at 200 p.p.m., after 1, 6 and 11 days' exposure. Asterisks, nominal level of significance after rejection (*, $P < 0.05$; **, $P < 0.01$; ***, $P < 0.001$). See text for explanation of solid bars.

These conclusions refer to a total pattern of behaviour; even when this is not significantly affected, differences can sometimes be found in one or two of the separate categories of behaviour, so that there is what might be called a provisional discrimination. This is shown by the black inner bars of Fig. 4. Thus, after the first day of exposure to 50 p.p.m. of vinyl acetate there was a "provisional" difference, nominally significant at the one per cent level, in both of two replicate tests separately, but there was no significant discrimination when the data were combined. There were also provisional differences after exposure on the first day to 100, 200, and 500 p.p.m., but after further exposures to 100 and 200 p.p.m. the effects of the vapour disappeared.

These experiments used relatively few animals, so it is possible that these provisional indications would have been significant with more observations; but their main interest lies in the fact that in nearly every case the behaviour increased by vinyl acetate included either submission to the other rat or escape away from him (Table I). In other words, although a fairly high concentration of the vapour was required to produce a definite effect, the indications were consistent. Although the indications were transient, their similarity at different concentrations suggests that they might also have occurred at concentrations below 50 p.p.m.

Nevertheless, if the effect of vinyl acetate on behaviour is important, I would expect it to be more clearly revealed. The rats could quite obviously smell the vapour, but they seemed to habituate to it quite quickly. The possible harmful effects of a substance should not be confused with its role as a stimulus for the Pavlovian "orientation reflex" when the animal can detect its presence. Although 50 p.p.m. is quite likely not a "no-effect level", my opinion is that it was not an unreasonable level for the tentative TLV. At this concentration there has been no adverse industrial experience, although on the basis of an experiment with human volunteers (Deese and Joyner, 1969), a tentative TLV of 10 p.p.m. has recently been officially recommended (American Conference of Governmental Industrial Hygienists, 1969).

It is not likely that any single behavioural method will be ideal for all possible effects. Observation of social behaviour was more sensitive than other behavioural methods for some effects of

TABLE I

BEHAVIOURAL CATEGORIES SIGNIFICANTLY ALTERED BY EXPOSURE OF RATS TO VINYL ACETATE VAPOUR

Vapour concentration

	50 p.p.m. Test a	50 p.p.m. Combined Test b	100 p.p.m.	200 p.p.m.	500 p.p.m.
Significant difference in behaviour	Provisional**	Provisional**	Provisional**	Provisional**	Provisional*
Behaviour increased	Escape	Submission	Submission	Escape, aggression	Submission
Behaviour decreased	Investigation	Maintenance		Submission	Aggression
Length of exposure	1 day	1 day	1 day	1 day	1 day
Significant difference in behaviour	No significant discrimination	Provisional**	No significant discrimination	No significant discrimination	Significant $P < 0.05$***
Behaviour increased		Sexual maintenance			Submission, maintenance
Behaviour decreased	Sexual maintenance				5 (of 6) others
Length of exposure	13–14 days		9 days	6 and 11 days	3 days

Not significant overall:
* "Provisional" at $P < 0.05$.
** "Provisional" at $P < 0.01$.
*** Significant overall; after rejection, $P < 0.001$.

nicotine. However, it is probably less useful than some operant schedules or exploration tests for other drug effects, certainly in measuring them once they have been detected; but the same is true of toxicological evidence produced by any single method. The subtler effects from low dosages may be objective, but their interpretation remains a matter of judgment, for which our criteria are still fairly arbitrary.

SUMMARY

A few chemicals have specific effects on behaviour, in that an appropriate test can reveal behavioural changes at doses where the underlying physiological and molecular changes are difficult to detect or of otherwise doubtful significance. For example, nicotine affects the behaviour of laboratory rats slightly but specifically at a dose of 25 μg/kg subcutaneously, which is estimated to be equivalent to the dose inhaled by a man smoking a cigarette. We have shown this by a test in which male rats are housed in pairs, separated for a few hours each week-day, and observed for 5 minutes on return to the home cage. The acts and postures displayed by the rats are tape-recorded, and any differences in pattern between experimentals and controls analysed by a multivariable statistical method.

However, behavioural effects of most chemicals are likely to be only secondary to damage to some other physiological system or to pain, etc. An example may be methylene bis thiocyanate. There was no effect on the social behaviour of rats at a dose of 0·5 mg/kg intraperitoneally, but 1 mg/kg caused the rats to show probable signs of pain and a reduction in activity consistent with the compound's local irritant effect.

Even where behavioural effects in animals are not clear-cut they can still be useful in setting safe limits for human exposure to industrial chemicals. Thus vinyl acetate, used industrially on a large scale, has a mildly irritant action on the eyes, nose, and lungs of rats, observable at concentrations above about 100 p.p.m. A tentative TLV of 50 p.p.m. was therefore suggested, which in practice appeared adequate. The social behaviour test in rats showed definite effects after three daily five-hour exposures to 500 p.p.m., and non-significant indications of similar effects after one day at 500 p.p.m., and in one test at

50 p.p.m. There was only a transient effect at 100 and 200 p.p.m., so the TLV of 50 p.p.m. for vinyl acetate seemed reasonable, but was quite probably not a "no-effect" level. However, subsequent American experiments with human volunteers, who can detect the compound at levels down to 0·5 p.p.m., recently led to a tentative TLV of 10 p.p.m. being proposed.

REFERENCES

AMERICAN CONFERENCE OF GOVERNMENTAL INDUSTRIAL HYGIENISTS (1969). *Threshold Limit Values for Airborne Contaminants.* Cincinnati, Ohio.
ARMITAGE, A. K., HALL, G. H., and MORRISON, C. F. (1968). *Nature, Lond.,* **217,** 331–334.
BOISSIER, J. R., and SIMON, P. (1967). In *Neurotoxicity of Drugs,* pp. 9–29. Amsterdam: Excerpta Medica Foundation.
BOVET, D., BOVET-NITTI, F., and OLIVERIO, A. (1967). *Ann. N.Y. Acad. Sci.,* **142,** 261–267.
CLARK, M. S. G. (1969). *Br. J. Pharmac.,* **35,** 367P.
DEESE, D. E., and JOYNER, R. E. (1969). *Am. ind. Hyg. Ass. J.,* **30,** 449–457.
DOMINO, E. F. (1967). *Ann. N.Y. Acad. Sci.,* **142,** 216–244.
GAGE, J. C. (1967). *Imperial Chemical Industries Limited, Industrial Hygiene Research Laboratories Report* TR/586.
GINZEL, K. H. (1967). *Ann. N.Y. Acad. Sci.,* **142,** 101–120.
GOFMEKLER, V. A. (1960). *Gig. Sanit.,* **25,** 9–15, *cited by* RYAZANOV, V. A. (1962). *Archs envir. Hlth,* **5,** 480–494.
GRANT, E. C., and MACKINTOSH, J. H. (1963). *Behaviour,* **21,** 246–259.
HALL, G. H. (1970). *Br. J. Pharmac.,* **38,** 271–286.
HOFF, E. C., and HOCKMAN, C. H. (1967). *Ann. N.Y. Acad. Sci.,* **142,** 121–125.
LIM, R. K. S., and GUZMAN, F. (1968). In *Pain,* pp. 119–152, ed. Soulairac, A., Cahn, J., and Charpentier, J. New York: Academic Press.
MEDVED, L. I., SPYNU, E. I., and KAGAN, Iu. S. (1964). *Residue Reviews,* **6,** 42–74.
RAO, C. R. (1952). *Advanced Statistical Methods in Biometric Research,* pp. 246. New York: Wiley.
SILVERMAN, A. P. (1967). *Imperial Chemical Industries Limited, Industrial Hygiene Research Laboratories Report* IHR/221.
SILVERMAN, A. P. (1970). *Anim. Behav.,* in press.

DISCUSSION

Boyland: Has anyone been able to define the effect of nicotine on man's behaviour or performance?

Silverman: In a government social survey, McKennell and Thomas (1967) found that different people smoked in different circumstances.

Spinks: There are components of the smoking habit other than the pharmacological one. You would not ascribe all the effects of smoking to the nicotine alone, I take it?

Silverman: No, but Hall (1970) showed that almost all the effects on the central nervous system (CNS) in his cat preparations were due to the nicotine. It also has to be explained why people do smoke cigarettes with nicotine and find that cigarettes with a very low nicotine content are unsatisfactory.

Beckett: The metabolism varies with the route and rate of administration of nicotine. Have you looked at nornicotine?

Silverman: No, but I have looked at synthetic compounds which do not have any behavioural effects.

Spinks: Can an effect which you believe to be on aggression or submission be isolated from other behavioural effects in an experiment intended primarily to measure these?

Silverman: In an experimental situation in which rats show aggression they will also show many other sorts of behaviour.

Spinks: I was thinking of a rank-order experiment. We use a very simple one: two rats are put in a pool of water with a small escape column on which only one can climb. In this situation it is possible to show which is the "top" rat of two, and the ranking can be altered by drugs. That type of situation could be used as a follow-up test to the one you are using.

Silverman: That would be an interesting experiment. I know of no good experiments to show that dominance in a competitive situation for escape or for food is the same as dominance expressed in terms of aggressive behaviour.

Albert: With a chemically administered agent such as cigarette smoke, withdrawal may be the most important effect. Bertrand Russell said about his pipe smoking that it didn't make him happy to smoke, it made him unhappy to stop.

King: Dr Silverman, you showed that the major effects of vinyl acetate were on escape and submission. In some previous work (Silverman, 1966) you picked out these two items of behaviour as being specifically affected by chlorpromazine. To what extent do your measures discriminate between certain drugs; and on the basis of chlorpromazine having a similar profile to vinyl acetate, to what extent would you consider chlorpromazine to be hazardous at the particular dose at which you tested it?

Silverman: The profile was not quite the same; chlorpromazine has some additional actions which vinyl acetate has not.

King: Nevertheless escape and submission were the most significant parameters.

Silverman: Yes, but the effects of chlorpromazine were clear-cut; those of vinyl acetate were tentative. If chlorpromazine were administered not therapeutically but at random, then it would be toxic. What is called harmful depends on the situation.

Paget: All these methods, including those that Dr Brimblecombe was speaking about earlier, are really screening mechanisms, and as such should lead on to analytical tests which would give an understanding of a potential hazard. That this is not so is demonstrated by Dr Silverman's results with nicotine. I do not believe that these or any other tests can be used to decide whether nicotine is a permissible environmental chemical. However, smoking may well be psychotoxic as well as toxic in a more conventional way, and one would be ill-advised to pass nicotine if it were an unknown candidate for wide use.

Brimblecombe: With a drug like nicotine, whose pharmacology one understands, it is possible to do the classical type of pharmacological experiments. Hall (1970) showed that certain effects of nicotine and tobacco smoke on the EEG in the cat were blocked by mecamylamine. Did you use other nicotinic agents, and did you try to block the effect of nicotine with nicotinic antagonists?

Silverman: I did not use nicotinic antagonists but I have done similar experiments with other drugs. The most similar drug to nicotine was benactyzine, which is anticholinergic, whereas nicotine is predominantly cholinergic (Silverman, 1966).

Spinks: Benactyzine is predominantly antimuscarinic.

Steinberg: How good is the correlation between "acute" and "chronic" toxic doses of different compounds?

Paget: This varies, obviously, from compound to compound, but acute tests cannot be the sole basis for the prediction of effects in man.

Spinks: The interesting case is where you do these tests on an unknown compound. You must first say whether the probable effects in man are beneficial, harmful or negligible, and then make a dose statement. This is extraordinarily difficult. Much of the toxicology we are normally concerned with requires predictions to be made from it. Often our experiments allow this. But I do not believe that the experiments you have described do allow this prediction to be made.

Silverman: True. In screening tests one aims to find an effect that can be used therapeutically without the presence of other detectable effects.

Spinks: No drug that we have ever passed for clinical trial has been harmless in all our animal tests. The balance between efficacy and safety must be reasonable

REFERENCES

HALL, G. H. (1970). *Br. J. Pharmac.*, **38,** 271–286.
McKENNELL, A. C., and THOMAS, R. K. (1967). *Government Social Survey: Adults' and Adolescents' Smoking Habits and Attitudes.* London: HMSO.
SILVERMAN, A. P. (1966). *Behaviour,* **27,** 1–38.

BEHAVIOURAL SENSITIVITY TO DRUGS IN THE LABORATORY RAT

ALAN R. KING

Medical Research Council Neuropharmacology Unit, The Medical School, Birmingham

THERE appear to be two kinds of drug which can influence animal behaviour; those like amphetamine which affect all types of behaviour (Weiss and Laties, 1962), and those which have a specific effect, such as ACTH which appears to affect only fear-motivated behaviour (Levine and Jones, 1965; de Wied, 1966). But although it is possible to classify some drugs in this way, the specificity of others depends on the nature of the environment in which they are tested. The barbiturates, for example, might be classified as having general behavioural properties because of their effect on afferently induced arousal thresholds (Bradley and Key, 1958), or as having specific properties because of their effect on the conditioned emotional response (Geller and Seifter, 1962). A specific effect is obtained by training a hungry animal to lever-press for food reward; when this behaviour has stabilized, a tone is introduced which is terminated by an unavoidable electric shock. After several tone-shock pairings, the onset of the tone is sufficient to suppress the mean rate of lever-pressing during its presence. After the administration of small doses of a barbiturate, tone-control over response-suppression is lost and the animal continues to lever-press despite receiving a shock.

The experiments which demonstrate the general and specific properties of the barbiturates differ in many ways; for example, threshold experiments explore a range of effective stimulus intensities, whereas the conditioned emotional response experiments involve two kinds of behaviour controlled by stimuli which differ in strength. In conditioned emotional response experiments, an increase in response threshold might be expected to yield specific behavioural effects because two classes of behaviour are being sampled at different distances from the individual thresholds. If the degree of stimulus control over the appetitive and aversive components of the conditioned emotional response is varied systematically, effects on both types of behaviour might be observed. This hypothesis was investigated using a multiple reinforcement schedule in which rats alternated between lever-pressing to avoid shock in response to one stimulus, followed, after an interval of 15 seconds, by lever-pressing to obtain water in response to another stimulus. So that the response strength aspect of the conditioned emotional response could be isolated, this experimental situation contained no programmed competition between responses. Response strength was manipulated by varying the amount of water given to an animal 40 minutes before a test session and by varying the intensity of the shock. Similar methods have been used before to investigate this problem but the results have not been consistent, probably because the response strength has not been effectively controlled (Ray, 1963; Barry and Miller, 1965; King, 1968). Two experiments were carried out with amylobarbitone sodium. Chlorpromazine was also studied because its effect on the threshold for behavioural arousal in response to a sensory stimulus is similar to that of the barbiturates (Bradley and Key, 1958), but its effects on the conditioned emotional response are inconsistent (Gollub and Brady, 1965).

RESULTS

Fig. 1 shows the effect on water-approach and shock-avoidance responses of varying the water-deprivation state and the shock-intensity. These results are for a sample of 18 animals tested twice on successive days in each experimental condition. An analysis of variance showed a significant effect of each water-deprivation level ($F=32 \cdot 12$, $d.f.=2/192$, $P<0 \cdot 001$). In addition, the effects of varying the water-deprivation generalized to the alternate shock-avoidance response, though not to the same degree. A similar analysis of the shock-intensity did not discriminate between shock levels, although the overall response to shock-avoidance was significantly lower than that to the alternate water-approach response ($F=38 \cdot 80$, $d.f.=1/192$, $P<0 \cdot 001$). As there was no significant difference between each test day,

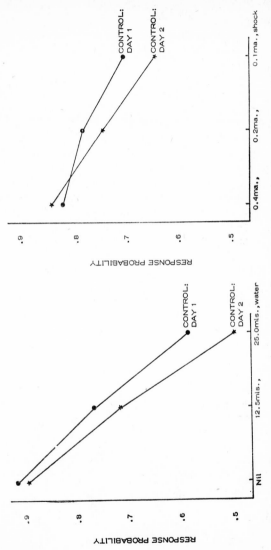

FIG. 1. Effects of varying the shock-intensity and water-deprivation state on the occurrence of shock-avoidance and water-approach responses. ma: milliamperes.

this indicated that day one could be used as a baseline control for day two in any subsequent drug investigation.

After the initial control studies had been completed two rats were discarded and the remaining animals were divided into four equal groups. Each group was tested with either amylobarbitone or chlorpromazine: one group after being exposed to variations in water-deprivation, the other after variations in shock-intensity. Two doses of each drug were given subcutaneously (10 and 20 mg/kg amylobarbitone; 0·375 and 0·750 mg/kg chlorpromazine) 20 minutes before each experiment. In the water-deprivation experiments, the injections took place 20 minutes after the animals had been watered, by which time all the water had been drunk. Each group was treated as a separate experiment in the subsequent analysis of variance.

In both the shock-intensity and water-deprivation experiments chlorpromazine had statistically significant effects ($P < 0·001$). The sensitivity of one shock or water level in relation to the others was indicated by the Treatment × Level first-order interaction term (Shock: $F = 14·81$, $d.f. = 2/6$, $P < 0·01$; Water: $F = 4·78$, $d.f. = 2/6$, NSS). The results of this analysis showed that as the shock-intensity was decreased the animal became increasingly sensitive to the drug, whereas after water-deprivation the effect of the drug remained constant irrespective of the control level. The non-significant Treatment × Type-of-Response interaction term indicated that the effects of varying the shock-intensity generalized to the alternate water-approach task. The main effects for chlorpromazine are summarized in Fig. 2 and those for amylobarbitone in Fig. 3. The effect of amylobarbitone was significant in the shock and water variation experiment ($P < 0·001$) The Treatment × Level interaction term, which indicates the sensitivity of one level of shock-intensity or water-deprivation in relation to the others, was significant only for the group exposed to variations in shock intensity ($F = 17·25$, $d.f. = 2/6$, $P < 0·01$). This result, which was similar to that for the chlorpromazine-treated, shock-intensity variation group, again indicated that as shock-intensity was decreased the animal became increasingly sensitive to the drug. Also the shock-intensity variation effect again generalized to the alternate water-approach task, as shown by a non-significant Treatment × Type-of-Response interaction term.

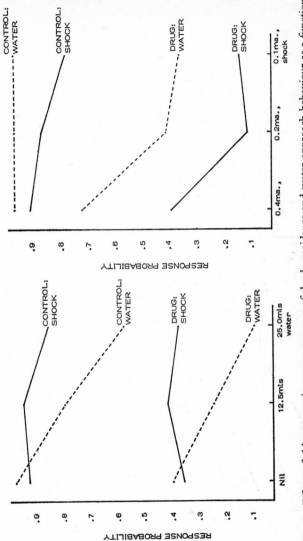

Fig. 2. Effects of chlorpromazine on occurrence of shock-avoidance and water-approach behaviour as a function of drive strength.

46 ALAN R. KING

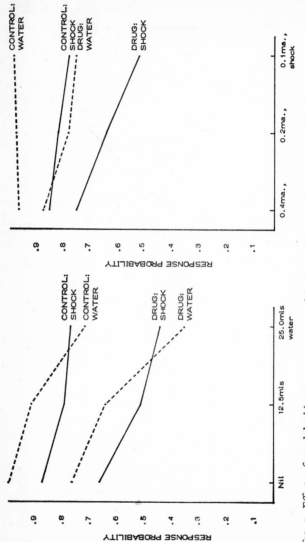

Fig. 3. Effects of amylobarbitone on occurrence of shock-avoidance and water-approach behaviour as a function of drive strength.

DISCUSSION

It may be concluded from the results of these experiments that chlorpromazine and amylobarbitone had similar effects in the experimental situation, both for the level and type of response. Since these two drugs have different effects when given to animals on a conditioned emotional response reinforcement schedule, the variables which were studied in these experiments were not likely to be those which would account for this difference. The fact that both drugs had similar effects is consistent with the results of previous studies in which it was shown that pentobarbitone and chlorpromazine raised the threshold for afferently induced behavioural arousal (Bradley and Key, 1958). Presumably, the factor which differentiates the effects of the barbiturates from the phenothiazines in the conditioned emotional response situation is the occurrence of response competition. It is interesting that both amylobarbitone and chlorpromazine caused changes in the alternate water-approach response after shock-intensity variation which were related to the size of the effect on the manipulated response. Similar kinds of drug-environment interaction have been observed before (King, 1964).

It is not clear why avoidance behaviour became increasingly sensitive to both drugs with decreasing stimulus control, whereas water-variation had no such effect. It is possible that the increase in the number of shocks between control and drug conditions tells the animal more about what shock level is being used than is the case under control conditions, where few shocks occur. In an experimental situation where it is the amount of water that is being varied, this information is available to the animal before the experiment begins. On the other hand, shock-avoidance behaviour may differ from water-approach behaviour in ways which are not effectively controlled by matching response probabilities. My colleague Peter Simson and I have observed water-approach and shock-avoidance behaviour over a range of response probability conditions. These observations were made either by videotaping or by making a sound commentary of the behaviour and analysing the motor patterns associated with each response. So far we have looked at 12 animals in a number of shock-intensity and water-deprivation situations.

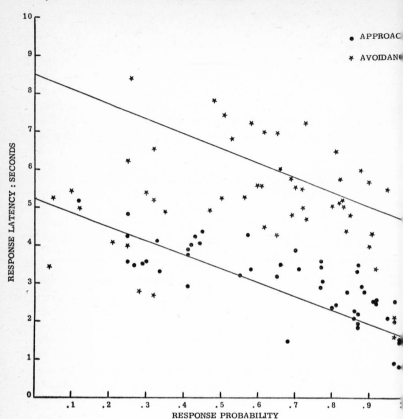

FIG. 4. Latency of approach and avoidance responses as
function of response probability.

Fig. 4 shows the mean time taken to execute each response during
a one-hour session. When this time is compared with response
probability (the regression line is fitted by eye) it is clear that
response latency for shock-avoidance is twice as long as for
water-approach. Identification of the actual motor patterns
indicates that this difference is not due to the same patterns taking
longer to execute, since different patterns are involved. The
movement patterns can be broken down into ambulation,

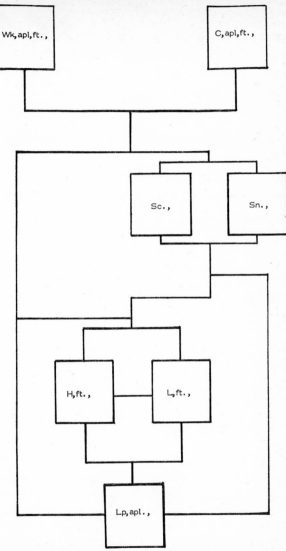

Fig. 5. Water-approach response pathway. *C*: crouch;
H: hold; *L*: lick; *Lp*: lever-press; *Sc*: scratch; *Sn*: scan;
Wk: walk; *apl*: approach lever; *ft*: fountain.

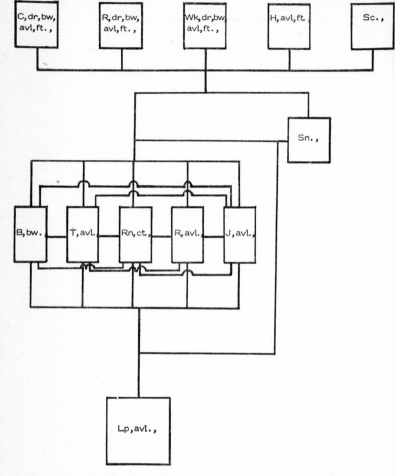

FIG. 6. Shock-avoidance response pathway. *B*: bite;
C: crouch; *H*: hold; *J*: jump; *Lp*: lever-press; *R*: rear
Rn: run; *Sn*: scan; *T*: touch; *Wk*: walk; *avl*: avoidance lever;
bw: back-wall; *ct*: circuit; *dr*: door; *ft*: fountain.

manipulation and maintenance postures. Ambulation includes walk, run, jump, rear, crouch, scan, and flinch; manipulation includes bite, hold, lick, touch, and lever-press; maintenance includes wash, groom, gnaw, and scratch, a total of 15 postures. Each of these components has a direction which locates its place of occurrence in the Skinner box, for example, at the fountain, lever, circuit, light, door, floor, ceiling and walls. The data shown in Figs. 5 and 6 summarize all the possible sequences of motor activity and link the onset of a particular trial to its termination by a correct lever-press, either on the approach lever or the avoidance lever. Inter-trial activity is not shown in Figs. 5 and 6; note that the water-approach response consists of fewer components and fewer alternative pathways than the shock-avoidance response, which has a complex structure particularly in relation to mid-trial events. Whether this complexity accounts for the increasing sensitivity to drugs with decreasing stimulus control is currently being investigated.

SUMMARY

To examine the effects on two kinds of instrumental behaviour, possibly related to the conditioned emotional response, some experiments were carried out in which the stimuli, shock-intensity and water-deprivation, were systematically varied. Chlorpromazine (0·375 and 0·750 mg/kg) and amylobarbitone sodium (10 and 20 mg/kg) were administered in each stimulus experiment. Similar effects were obtained with both drugs; water-deprivation interacted with the drug in an additive manner, whereas shock-intensity showed a multiplicative relationship. Since both drugs had similar effects, the type and intensity of stimulus control do not seem to be the variables which distinguish the action of chlorpromazine from that of amylobarbitone on the conditioned emotional response. It was concluded that shock-avoidance became more sensitive to both drugs with decreasing stimulus control, whereas the effect of water-deprivation remained constant. In another experiment it was shown that shock-avoidance behaviour had a longer latency than water-approach when matched for probability of occurrence, and that this effect was related to the structure of the response rather than to the time taken for its occurrence.

Acknowledgement

I am grateful to my Director, Professor P. B. Bradley, for encouraging me to carry out these experiments.

REFERENCES

BARRY, H., and MILLER, N. E. (1965). *J. comp. physiol. Psychol.*, **59**, 18–24.

BRADLEY, P. B., and KEY, B. J. (1958). *Electroenceph. clin. Neurophysiol.*, **10**, 97–104.

GELLER, I., and SEIFTER, J. (1962). *J. Pharmac. exp. Ther.*, **136**, 284–288.

GOLLUB, L., and BRADY, J. (1965). *A. Rev. Pharmac.*, **5**, 235–262.

KING, A. R. (1964). *Psychopharmacologia*, **6**, 338–346.

KING, A. R. (1968). *Physiol. Behav.*, **3**, 935–939.

LEVINE, S., and JONES, L. E. (1965). *J. comp. physiol. Psychol.*, **59**, 357–360.

RAY, O. S. (1963). *Psychopharmacologia*, **4**, 326–342.

WEISS, B., and LATIES, V. G. (1962). *Pharmac. Rev.*, **14**, 1–36.

WIED, D. DE (1966). *Proc. Soc. exp. Biol. Med.*, **122**, 28–32.

DISCUSSION

Weiskrantz: Were the avoidance pathways that you plotted characteristic of well-trained animals?

King: Yes. The whole training procedure takes about 60 hours.

Silverman: Ray (1963) compared chlorpromazine and pento-barbitone in a similar two-lever test. Chlorpromazine inhibited the shock-avoidance response without altering pressing on a second lever for a milk reward, whereas pentobarbitone did not have a differential effect on the two levers. Ray (1964) repeated the experiments of Geller and Seifter (1960), in which pressing a single lever resulted in the rat receiving both food and shock. In both experiments, chlorpromazine reduced lever-pressing. In the two-lever experiment, the inhibition was selective, the rat accepted more shocks, suggesting that chlorpromazine *reduced* conditioned avoidance; in the single-lever experiment the inhibition suggested that the drug *increased* avoidance of shock. Have you any comments?

King: Our experiments were largely based on the work of Ray (1963) and Barry and Miller (1965). Ray's work is a good example of the problem of stimulus control in varying deprivation levels and varying shock-intensity. He looked at the behaviour of rats at one deprivation level, and he ran his experiments with the shock off. In this particular case he observed a selective effect of chlorpromazine on shock avoidance behaviour, that is, shock avoidance was eliminated whereas the alternate response for a food reward remained. The point of my data is that whether this happens or not is to some extent a function of the degree of water deprivation and the degree of shock. The presence or absence of selectivity depends on how one programmes the responses.

Boyland: Is it possible to correlate these results with any clinical effects of these two classes of drugs?

King: In these experiments I obtained similar effects with both drugs. Clinically barbiturates are poor drugs for the treatment of schizophrenia but chlorpromazine is effective. We are interested in finding ways of experimentally differentiating between these two classes of compound.

Boyland: Are barbiturates more rapidly metabolized and excreted than chlorpromazine?

Spinks: Amylobarbitone is fairly persistent, and for the duration of this experiment fairly large amounts would be present unmetabolized. It is also fairly persistent in man.

King: These experiments took place over one to one and a half hours.

Kety: Dr King, would you describe the effects of chlorpromazine and of barbiturates on two types of conditioned emotional response? I mean the operant conditioned emotional response that you have been working with and the kind of conditioned emotional response in which one simply observes the whole behaviour of the animal—crouching, pile-erection, defaecation and so on.

King: We have been using conditioned avoidance behaviour as a "substrate" for emotional behaviour. I am interested in the possibility that the type of schedule of reinforcement we are using bears some resemblance, in operational properties, to the conditioned emotional response procedure. I have only looked at shock-avoidance and water-approach behaviour in the operant situation. A number of studies on the effects of psychotropic drugs on ambulation and defaecation have been made but the results do not help me to distinguish a barbiturate from a phenothiazine (Brimblecombe, 1963; Kumar, 1968; Christmas and Maxwell, 1970; Marriott and Spencer, 1965).

Kety: In the operant behaviour experiment in which the animal was trained to lever-press for a food reward and this response was suppressed by the introduction of tone-shock pairings, was the response restored by appropriate doses of barbiturates but not by chlorpromazine?

King: That is correct. Grossman's (1961) is the only published study showing chlorpromazine and a barbiturate to have a similar effect in this situation.

Kety: One of the classical neurophysiological effects of barbiturates is an accentuation of the cortical evoked response, presumably by preferential block of the reticular-activating system. It was by using a barbiturate that Marshall, Woolsey and Bard (1941) were able to map the first cortical evoked responses. Barbiturates enhance the direct sensory pathways to the cortex but block the indirect pathways.

King: This effect implies that the animal's discriminative abilities are impaired by barbiturates, but we have no evidence to suggest that this is happening.

Kety: If by discriminative ability we mean something which depends on the direct sensory pathways, then those old neurophysiological experiments would have predicted that discriminative ability would not be impaired, because sensory pathways are not blocked. But if the indirect pathways to the central nervous system (CNS) and the cortex are those which are involved in affective behaviour, then these would be blocked by barbiturates and a change in this behaviour would occur. Barbiturates may act on the indirect pathways to block the conditioned emotional response.

King: I take the point; you are referring to Arousal Theory. I am concerned with the behavioural aspects of the problem. I have not yet found any neurophysiological concept which accounts for all the behavioural data. Arousal Theory is difficult to handle since it predicts facilitatory and inhibitory effects of depressant drugs as a function of stimulus intensity.

Kety: That is why it would be interesting to see what barbiturates do to the global conditioned emotional response. If your interpretation is correct barbiturates should be blocking the generalized emotional response—crouching, defaecation, pile-erection and so on. Then the mode of behaviour would simply be one small segment of the total effect of the barbiturate.

King: This could well be so. However, some recent work by Stein and Berger (1969) suggests that barbiturates may not necessarily be specific for the conditioned emotional response. In these experiments, amylobarbitone intensified the conditioned emotional response. We are interested in trying to pull these reinforcement schedules apart into their various components.

Silverman: The trouble with the arousal concept is the extreme difficulty of distinguishing general arousal from arousal of a specific kind of behaviour. There is some evidence (Kumar, 1968; Silverman, 1966) that barbiturates selectively reduce the behaviour that in man would be accompanied by the particular emotion of fear, and independently increase other kinds of behaviour such as exploration. It is this type of change in the differential response to relatively constant stimuli that makes generalized arousal so difficult to handle.

Weiskrantz: One can only applaud the effort to try to tease apart these factors. In the two situations that Professor Kety referred to, namely the old-fashioned conditioned emotional response situation and the suppression situation Dr King talked about, one is dealing with classical Pavlovian conditioning or, to use Skinnerian terminology, respondents. But there are difficulties in trying to pull classical conditioning apart by using instrumental avoidance conditioning or, in Skinnerian terminology, operant conditioning. There are many ways in which the two do not co-vary. For example, one can avoid cars in crossing the street perfectly calmly without getting the palpitations that are controlled by classical conditioning. Whether you call the palpitations "emotion" or not is not important. But in the instrumental avoidance situation a different kind of control is exercised over the behaviour This may be one reason why dissociation of drug effects occurs in the classical but not in the instrumental conditioning situation.

King: I agree completely. We did our experiments in an attempt to isolate some of the determinants of behaviour that Professor Kety is interested in. The point Professor Weiskrantz is making concerns the behaviour itself—a different circumstance.

Philp: What is the reason for the difference in the latency periods for the response to water-deprivation and shock-avoidance? One explanation might be that the rat is already by tradition knowledgeable about its need for water and there is no emotion, in general, if there is no water. Search for water is purposeful and devoid of panic. Whereas with shock the animal is trying to avoid pain. I thought the different patterns in these two situations were significant. Could the longer latency period for the response to shock-avoidance be due to the animal thrashing around in a small area because of pain and finally hitting the lever by chance?

King: No. This is a controlled response which is reproducible. I agree with Professor Weiskrantz's comment that a classical conditioning process is involved in the conditioned avoidance response. This might be related to the experience of punishment for pressing the lever in the early stages of conditioning when the animal was running round the box. A good deal of approach-avoidance conflict (Miller, 1944) is involved in pressing a lever to avoid shock.

Philp: I would have expected that the animal would quickly learn to avoid pain, but in fact it learned the response to water-deprivation more quickly.

King: We must distinguish between learning and performance. These animals learn to reach a high level of both shock-avoidance and water-approach response. The difference is that although there is a statistically equal chance of their being able to perform these responses, in practice they take longer to execute the shock-avoidance response than the water-approach response.

Joyce: Do you balance the order in which you shape the two responses? The results might differ, depending on whether you always shape the water response before the shock-avoidance response or *vice versa*.

King: I wish this were so because it would give us a way of controlling some of the aspects of the shock-avoidance behaviour. The order in which we shape the two responses makes no difference to the resulting structure of the behaviour. We normally condition the water-approach behaviour first because transfer between this and the acquisition of shock-avoidance behaviour is excellent, and there is poor transfer if we do it the other way round.

Joyce: Are the results consistent and reproducible?

King: Yes, provided the experiments are done in our laboratory.

Paget: Let us suppose that these two substances on which you have done tests and got results were unknown. On your tests what would you feel about releasing them into the environment?

King: These experiments were not carried out to define

behavioural toxicity, they were designed to find out what are the behavioural effects of the different drugs.

Steinberg: It has been argued that chlorpromazine and similar drugs could be regarded as "stretched-out" barbiturates which cause different effects with any one dose; with chlorpromazine the effects are different at different dose levels—they are dose-specific. This may explain why chlorpromazine is more useful clinically than the barbiturates (Steinberg, 1962).

Boyland: Chlorpromazine is slowly metabolized, giving a continuous and longer-lasting effect than the barbiturates; also it is less effective as an enzyme inducer than they are.

Spinks: These features probably depend on dose size rather than dose frequency. But the duration of action of different barbiturates is different. I would classify amylobarbitone as long-acting and secobarbitone sodium (Seconal) as short-acting.

Boyland: The advantage of a long-acting drug is that one does not have to rely on a high activity peak for the effect.

Spinks: The difference between the two is more subtle than that. Biochemically, the mode of action of short-acting and long-acting drugs may be different. For example, chlorpromazine has a greater specificity of action and amylobarbitone a more general depressant action.

Joyce: "Long activity" is a term that conceals rather than reveals. Biochemists tend to be impressed that a drug has a long duration of action if either the unchanged drug or its metabolites persists, whereas clinicians and behavioural psychologists are more impressed by persisting behavioural or clinical effects. Current attempts to correlate plasma levels with clinical or behavioural effects do not seem to be meeting with much success, possibly because even plasma is so far from the CNS in general and the specific sites where the drugs act in particular.

Beckett: Correlation between plasma or tissue levels and clinical effects depends on the type of drug and its mechanism of action. If it acts by an indirect effect on a number of enzyme systems, correlation between levels and effects is unlikely. But for some drugs, e.g. ethanol and certain CNS stimulants, such correlations are obtained, and as more drugs for which these correlations are valid are studied our ability to measure levels and effects will increase.

Joyce: This may be true for acute experiments, but the most interesting drugs clinically are those that are taken for long periods of time, have a relatively slow onset of action and an ill-defined spectrum of activity, and normally affect only abnormal subjects, that is, patients.

Beckett: It will be difficult to work out these correlations for the phenothiazines because they are extensively metabolized and some of the metabolites are active. The presence of many variables causes complications.

Paget: Any apprentice pharmacologist faced with two unknowns, one of which was a barbiturate and the other chlorpromazine, would be able to distinguish between them without too much difficulty.

Spinks: There is no trouble in distinguishing between them using an empirically derived test based on the prior existence of the two drugs. Unfortunately, we lack a rational theory to design such tests.

Weiskrantz: What is the predictive value of animal tests for toxicity in man? Obviously this question can only be answered if independent measures of toxicity are available. Behavioural scientists do not usually try to relate their work to toxicity as such, but occasionally independent measures of toxicity do exist. We have been dealing with monkeys in behavioural situations rather similar to those that we have heard about today. If an animal's behavioural rate of response is decreased on a particular day, the probability of his being ill the next day is high. This sort of assessment has far better predictive value than any other measure of gross behaviour. But this is not currently the object of our investigations; if it were perhaps we could begin to answer my question.

Paget: I agree. The same factor must always be studied in two situations. This is true for any toxicity study. But in behavioural studies the situation is particularly favourable because human behaviour is the one thing that everybody is interested in. We know of many behaviourally active substances, such as alcohol, the xanthines and so on; yet we are completely incapable of predicting, *de novo*, what effects a substance which has not been studied in man will have when given to man.

Weiskrantz: This is not necessarily so. My point was that usually only one half of the question of the predictive value of behavioural tests is receiving attention.

Venables: The application of behavioural studies in animals to human behaviour is not easy. Let me take an example. Dr Silverman said that one of the effects of nicotine was to reduce aggressive behaviour. If, for instance, the effect of nicotine on animals resembled a partial lesion of the amygdala, it might show up in man as a specific memory defect rather than as an emotional defect, and this is what we would have to investigate. The toxic effect might therefore be obscure, and unless one were looking for that particular defect one might miss it entirely.

REFERENCES

BARRY, H., and MILLER, N. E. (1965). *J. comp. physiol. Psychol.*, **59**, 18–21.

BRIMBLECOMBE, R. W. (1963). *Psychopharmacologia*, **4**, 139–147.

CHRISTMAS, A. J., and MAXWELL, D. R. (1970). *Neuropharmacology*, **9**, 17–30.

GELLER, I., and SEIFTER, J. (1960). *Psychopharmacologia*, **1**, 482–492.

GROSSMAN, S. P. (1961). *J. comp. physiol. Psychol.*, **54**, 517–521.

KUMAR, R. (1968). *Nature, Lond.*, **218**, 587–588.

MARRIOTT, A. S., and SPENCER, P. S. J. (1965). *Br. J. Pharmac. Chemother.*, **25**, 432–441.

MARSHALL, W., WOOLSEY, C. N., and BARD, P. (1941). *J. Neurophysiol.*, **4**, 1.

MILLER, N. E. (1944). In *Personality and the Behavior Disorders*, ed. Hunt, J. McV. New York: Ronald Press.

RAY, O. S. (1963). *Psychopharmacologia*, **4**, 326–342.

RAY, O. S. (1964). *Psychopharmacologia*, **5**, 136–146.

SILVERMAN, A. P. (1966). *Psychopharmacologia*, **10**, 155–171.

STEIN, L., and BERGER, B. D. (1969). *Science*, **166**, 253–256.

STEINBERG, H. (1962). In *Recent Advances in Pharmacology*, p. 77, ed. Robson, J. M., and Stacey, R. S. London: Churchill.

HEREDITY AND ENVIRONMENT AS CAUSES OF DISEASE

HARRY HARRIS

Galton Laboratory, University College London

HUMAN beings are exceedingly diverse. They differ in their normal physical, physiological and mental characteristics. They also differ in whether they develop particular diseases or other abnormalities. In part this diversity is a consequence of differences in their genetical constitutions, that is differences in the properties of the particular genes they have received from their parents. Indeed there is now a considerable body of evidence which suggests that no two people, with the exception of monozygotic twins, are exactly alike in their genetic endowments. Furthermore it seems that most genes exert their effects by directing the synthesis of enzymes and other proteins, and that it is in this way that they determine the metabolic and developmental processes which are characteristic of the species and of the individual. So each individual probably has his own unique enzyme and protein makeup.

But the manner in which the genetical constitution of an individual is expressed depends on the particular environmental circumstances in which he develops and in which he lives. And of course the environmental circumstances vary from one person to another and are always changing. So the individual diversity in human charactersitics and behaviour which we so readily observe must be considered as a complex product of both genetical and environmental factors.

This conclusion is not new; nevertheless it has remained curiously difficult to delineate in precise terms the manner in which genetical and environmental factors contribute to the causation of many human disorders. It is perhaps useful, therefore, to re-examine the problem in its simplest form by looking at a few selected conditions in which the effects of the genetical factors at the enzyme level have been elucidated, and in which the principal environmental factors affecting their expression in the organism as a whole are more or less understood.

Consider galactosaemia. In this condition there is a specific inability to metabolize the sugar galactose because of a genetically determined deficiency of the enzyme galactose-1-phosphate uridyl transferase. Galactose in the form of the disaccharide lactose is the major carbohydrate constituent of milk, and so in the usual course of events newborn infants will receive large amounts of it. If the transferase enzyme is lacking there is a block in galactose metabolism. Galactose accumulates in the blood and galactose-1-phosphate accumulates intracellularly. The consequences are severe. The infant fails to thrive, weight gain is slow, and eventually liver and brain damage and cataract formation occur. If, however, a diet free of galactose but adequate in other respects is fed to the infant a dramatic improvement occurs. Indeed, it appears that if the diagnosis is made sufficiently early, before irreversible damage has occurred, the infant will develop in a normal and healthy manner.

In a sense then, the condition can be regarded as an inborn inability of the infant to cope with one particular facet of his normal environment, namely lactose in milk. If the environment is modified appropriately the ill effects of the disability can be prevented. The individual will still lack the particular enzyme, but in his new environment this will not incommode him. He will, as it were, be predisposed without being clinically affected.

The condition known as herediatry fructose intolerance illustrates the same general point. Here there is a deficiency of the enzyme 'liver aldolase' (aldolase B) which is necessary for the normal metabolism of fructose. If fructose is excluded from the diet no harmful effects occur. Unlike galactose, fructose is not an obligatory feature of the normal diet of an infant. Consequently the manifestation and severity of the disease are more variable. An important factor appears to be the time at which breast feeding is discontinued. If an early change to artificial milk feeds with added sucrose is made, rapid deterioration in the infant's condition occurs, and should the nature of the abnormality not be recognized, irreversible damage may occur. If, however, the infant is not weaned until he is several months old he is often able to make a positive rejection of feeds which make him ill, and the peculiarity is more likely to be diagnosed. Furthermore such children tend to develop a strong aversion to sugar, sweets and fruit, and thus tend to protect themselves. This illustrates clearly how the severity of an inherited disease may depend on quite fortuitous and apparently unconnected factors in the infant's environment—in this case the time when breast feeding is discontinued. In passing one may also note that it also illustrates, in a somewhat dramatic manner, the way in which taste and food preferences of an individual may be a direct consequence of a specific enzyme abnormality.

A particularly clear example of the way in which environmental and genetical factors may interact in the causation of a disease process is provided by the condition known as favism. This has been known for many years as a severe form of recurrent haemolytic anaemia in which the attacks follow the ingestion of the fava bean. It is found particularly in the Middle East and certain parts of Southern Europe where the fava bean is a common feature of the diet. However, by no means all people who eat fava beans develop favism. Those that do have been shown to have a genetically determined deficiency of glucose-6-phosphate dehydrogenase. So to develop the disease an individual must carry the gene and eat the bean. Both genetical and environmental factors can thus be clearly seen as essential to the causation of the disease. In fact the matter is even more complex because not all individuals with the specific form of enzyme deficiency who eat fava beans develop overt haematological disease, and among those that do its severity can be variable. The detailed reasons for this are not known, but there is some evidence that other genetical factors may be involved as well as differences in the quantity and the form in which the beans are eaten.

We have little hesitation in regarding galactosaemia as a hereditary disease because it is manifest in all individuals with the appropriate genetical constitution. The environmental feature to which they are ill-adapted is universally present. The same is essentially true for hereditary fructose intolerance, except that here the environmental factor is somewhat more variable and this is reflected by variation in the severity of the clinical condition. It is not, however, possible to regard favism as purely genetical or purely environmental in origin, and this is probably true of many other clinical conditions.

Whether a disease tends to be regarded as primarily genetical or environmental in origin largely depends on the relative prevalence of the genetically determined predisposition to the condition, and also the particular environmental situation which elicits it. If the genetical predisposition is relatively rare, and the significant environmental factor is common or indeed universal— as is the case with galactosaemia—we say that the disease is inherited. If, however, the genetical predisposition is relatively common and the unfavourable environmental situation occurs infrequently, then the environmental factors appear as the most important causal agents.

An extreme example is scurvy. As far as we know all members of our own species and also other primates are incapable of synthesizing L-ascorbic acid (vitamin C). Consequently if for some reason their diet is deficient in this substance they develop scurvy. This is not the case in many other mammalian species which apparently can manage without an independent dietary source of L-ascorbic acid because they can synthesize it from D-glucose via the reaction sequence:

D-glucose→D-glucuronolactone→L-gulonolactone→L-ascorbic acid.

Evidently in man and other primates the enzyme activity capable of converting L-gulonolactone to L-ascorbic acid is lacking, presumably because the necessary gene has been lost in the course of evolution. So scurvy with good reason is considered to be a disease caused by an unfavourable environment, namely one in which the individual's diet is deficient in Vitamin C. But it can equally well be thought of as due to an inborn error of metabolism which we all happen to possess.

In some cases of course, both the inherited predisposition to a particular disease and also the specific environmental factors which elicit it may both be relatively uncommon. In these circumstances the disease is likely to be rare and very irregularly distributed, and it may not be apparent from family studies that hereditary factors are involved. A simple model of this kind of situation is the occurrence of the abnormality known as 'suxamethonium apnoea'. About one in 2,000 people are excessively sensitive to the drug suxamethonium which is often used to obtain muscular relaxation during surgery. This is because such individuals synthesize an atypical form of the enzyme serum cholinesterase which is much less effective in destroying the drug than the usual form, or because they fail to synthesize the enzyme in any significant amount. The muscular and consequently respiratory paralysis induced by the drug is under these circumstances excessively prolonged. However, unless exposed to this unusual and rather artificial feature of the environment, that is the drug suxamethonium, these people appear to be quite normal. Thus, both the rare genetical predisposition and the unusual environmental circumstances must occur together before an abnormal clinical state appears. It is not surprising that such a disorder may not at first sight appear to be familial.

If we survey the range of human disease and abnormalities we find at one extreme conditions such as sickle cell anaemia, phenylketonuria, haemophilia, muscular dystrophy and so on, which we regard as inherited disorders because all individuals who have the appropriate genes develop the condition. At the other extreme are the typically environmental diseases—such as the severe infections like plague, anthrax, typhus—in which it appears that virtually everyone who is sufficiently exposed to the unfavourable environmental agent develops the disease. But in between there are many disorders, often common ones, in which both genetical and environmental factors are apparently important. Typical examples are schizophrenia, diabetes mellitus and peptic ulcer. In each of these conditions there is good evidence for genetical predisposition, and it is also clear that only a fraction of those genetically predisposed actually develop the condition. But we do not know the nature or the primary effects of the genes involved, nor can we clearly define the particular features of the environment which cause some individuals, but not others, among those genetically predisposed to develop the condition.

The elements of the situation can be illustrated by a simple diagram (Fig. 1). The area encompassed by the outer circle represents a population, and that enclosed by the inner circle those individuals in the population genetically predisposed to develop a particular kind of disease. The two lines drawn from the centre to the periphery divide the whole population into those who are exposed to environmental factors which tend to elicit the abnormality (in this case the smaller group), and those who are not so exposed. Only the small segment of the population who are both genetically predisposed and also subjected to the unfavourable environmental situation actually develop the clinical disorder.

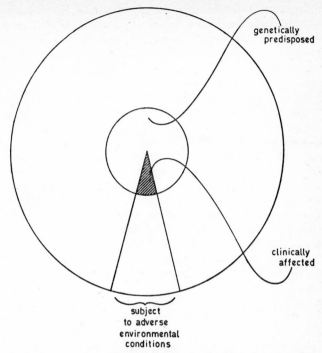

FIG. 1. Diagram illustrating in a simple form the roles of genetical predisposition and adverse environmental factors in the causation of disease (see text). Area bounded by outer circle represents a population, and the area enclosed within the inner circle those individuals in the population who are genetically predisposed to develop a particular kind of disease. The two lines from the centre to the periphery enclose a segment of the population subject to some particular environmental conditions that may elicit the disease. The hatched part of the segment represents those individuals who actually develop the disease.

The practical significance of this kind of formulation is that it emphasizes how if by genetical research one could find ways of identifying the individuals in the population who are predisposed to a particular condition, then one would be provided with a powerful tool with which to discover critical environmental factors. In effect one would be able to ask what significant differences exist or have existed between the environmental circumstances of the predisposed individuals who actually develop the disease, and those who do not. And if these environmental circumstances can be recognized they can hopefully be adjusted in an appropriate manner for the genetically predisposed individuals before the clinical abnormality develops.

The point may be simply illustrated by recent work (see Harris, 1970 for references) on the inherited variations of a particular serum protein which forms part of the α_1 globulin fraction and acts as a specific inhibitor of trypsin, elastase and possibly other proteolytic enzymes. About one in 5000 people appear to be homozygous for a gene which produces a marked deficiency of this serum protein. These individuals are peculiarly prone to develop severe primary emphysema in early adult life, but only about half of these susceptible individuals actually develop the disease. Thus a detailed comparison of the modes of life of the healthy and emphysematous individuals with this specific genetically determined peculiarity may be expected to uncover the particular environmental factors which precipitate the disorder.

Clearly for any particular condition the fraction of the population genetically predisposed may be very small or quite large, and the proportion exposed to the adverse environmental situations can vary similarly. Furthermore, one must expect that often many different genes can give rise in one way or another to a particular kind of predisposition, and since their effects will not be identical the degree of predisposition may vary and be graded in severity. Similarly the relevant environmental factors are likely to vary in strength. So the lines shown in Fig. 1 should be regarded as fuzzy rather than sharp.

Nevertheless this simple minded, if diagrammatic, approach is perhaps a useful way of thinking about the possible role of genetic and environmental factors in determining abnormal states, and it provides the kind of model which it would be desirable to keep in mind when considering the exposure of human populations to new chemicals or drugs.

REFERENCES

For detailed references see, HARRIS, H. (1970). *The Principles of Human Biochemical Genetics*. Amsterdam: North-Holland.

DISCUSSION

Boyland: Can the biochemical lesions associated with neuro-logical or behavioural effects be corrected by nutritional additions or made worse by environmental chemicals?

Harris: I believe that neurological or psychiatric disabilities ultimately have some kind of biochemical explanation. If one could find out what this is, one might have a clue as to how an environmental chemical could modify or bring out a particular clinical disorder.

Boyland: Aren't some disorders of tryptophan and phenyl-alanine metabolism particularly associated with behavioural effects?

Harris: I am not convinced of this. Many abnormalities in other areas of metabolism could equally well be concerned with such disorders, but suitable techniques for detecting them may have either not been developed or not extensively applied.

Sandler: We are investigating a model experimental situation for migraine, a neurological disorder presumably genetically determined, which remains latent until its characteristic sequence of clinical features is triggered off by a dietary constituent; in fact, a minority of patients with migraine are sensitive to tyramine-containing foods, particularly cheese. Hanington (1967) has shown this quite elegantly. These patients are unable to conjugate tyramine (Smith, Kellow and Hanington, 1970). They appear to absorb it in greater amount from the gastrointestinal tract so that more tyramine tends to get into the circulation (Sandler *et al.*, 1970). Tyramine liberates catecholamines (Kopin, 1966) and dopamine (Bonham Carter *et al.*, 1970) from their binding sites. These amines may not only be implicated in the neuro-vascular migraine sequence, but their liberation in certain subjects by dietary constituents which traverse the blood–brain barrier may give us a lead in elucidating some behavioural disturbances.

Cowley: In South East Asia many of the children are unable to break down lactose (Flatz, Saengudom and Sanguanbhokhai, 1969) after the age of about four years. This implies that a change has occurred because of genetic or environment factors, or an interaction between them.

Harris: It seems perfectly plausible to expect that there are differences in the synthesis of the enzymes, and that the genes that cause these differences will vary in frequency from population to population.

Cowley: The important point is that there is a time sequence.

Harris: We know too little as yet about enzyme changes during development. It would be difficult to work these out for this abnormality because intestine biopsies for enzyme assay would be needed sequentially in time, not only from affected individuals but also from their families.

Spinks: These deficiency diseases usually arise because of complete absence of the enzyme. Presumably chemical inhibition of the same enzyme would give a milder version of the same disease. Is there any evidence of this in any of these diseases, for example in the patients with abnormal monoamine oxidase synthesis who react adversely to cheese?

Harris: There might be inherited differences in monoamine oxidase synthesis. Some people would have the deficiency for genetic reasons, others because they were receiving the appropriate drug or food.

Beckett: When an atypical cholinesterase is present is the rate of hydrolysis of other esters of choline reduced?

Harris: Yes, but this varies in degree from substrate to substrate. Subjects with this abnormality are perfectly healthy and, as far as I know, no abnormalities in their fat metabolism have been recorded. Furthermore, we do not know what the normal metabolic function of serum cholinesterase is.

Marley: Environmental and individual factors can coexist and the outcome still be unpredictable. For example, the combination of an environmental factor (tyramine eaten in cheese) together with an individual factor (inhibition or lack of monoamine oxidase) does not necessarily mean the subject will have a hypertensive "cheese reaction". If the cheese is taken on its own then a hypertensive crisis is more likely than if the cheese forms only part of a substantial meal. If the amine oxidase inhibitor is of the amine type, such as tranylcypromine, and is taken immediately before the cheese, then there may be little or no pressor effect because tranylcypromine is located at the sites where tyramine would normally act, that is, there is competition or tachyphylaxis for the sites. These are only a few of a number of known factors contributing to the reaction (Blackwell and Marley, 1966; Blackwell *et al.*, 1967).

Sandler: If monoamine oxidase is blocked in the patients I mentioned earlier (p. 67) with defective tyramine conjugation, one may run into adverse reactions which are even more severe than they would have been if the "safety-valve" of conjugation had been intact.

Harris: Even after all this time, we are only beginning to understand the simplest situations where most of the genetic effect is represented by a deficiency or peculiarity of one enzyme, and most of the environmental effect comes from one particular source.

Joyce: In subjects who are dependent on barbiturates, prolonged usage causes induction of microsomal enzymes. The subject has learned, in consequence, to take increasing doses of barbiturate. If he then stops taking the drug, or is stopped, and does not know that the enzyme is meanwhile de-inducing, he may subsequently go back to using the same high doses as he was using previously, often with disastrous results.

Steinberg: Professor Harris, you mentioned babies who had hereditary fructose intolerance and rejected foods that contained fructose. Are there any other examples of this sort of syndrome?

Harris: This is the only well-authenticated example that I know of.

Steinberg: Could this sort of phenomenon be investigated in laboratory animals?

Harris: Yes, if one could find a suitable experimental situation.

Steinberg: Richter, Holt and Barelane (1938) and Katz (1953) showed some years ago that animals will select "balanced" diets if given the opportunity, but I know of no recent work that is directly relevant to these problems.

Marley: My son had severe gluten intolerance and we were faced with the quandary of when to put him back on a normal diet. He eventually decided for himself by hurling his gluten-free food on to the ground and refusing to eat it any more. He ate a normal meal and we stood by waiting for a nasty crisis which never happened.

Albert: The existence of a rare genetic susceptibility to a particular environmental hazard bedevils the problem of defining safe limits of exposure. On the other hand, the fact that a few individuals show severe toxicity on this basis affords a measure of consolation. For example, thousands of children in the slums of

New York City undoubtedly eat lead paint; a few hundred of these develop lead poisoning. The question comes up as to whether or not a large part of the slum population has various degrees of CNS damage due to the ingestion of lead. What you have discussed, Professor Harris, suggests that there may be relatively few individuals who, on a genetic basis, have a very high susceptibility to lead poisoning.

Harris: We should not read too much into this because when one is looking for examples it is the all-or-none situations which stand out most clearly. In many cases there is likely to be a graded situation with varying individual susceptibilities to a particular environmental agent.

Spinks: Which enzymes are inhibited in subjects who show lead toxicity?

Albert: I do not know.

Boyland: Lead poisoning causes porphyrinuria which may be associated with mental deficiency.

Barnes: The lead level in city air is not very high. There is up to 2 mg of lead per day in our food.

Boyland: But even a small amount of lead may be toxic to a small proportion of the population.

Albert: I was not implying that there is a genetic predisposition to lead poisoning only that in some circumstances one might hope that there is. Large numbers of slum children are probably over-exposed to lead.* The question is whether those with overt poisoning are only the most severely affected of the much larger numbers who are injured, that is, whether they are the tip of the iceberg, or whether there are two distinct population groups, one with high susceptibility and the other with negligible susceptibility to the toxic effects of lead.

Kety: I do not know if the amount of lead in the atmosphere is dangerous or not, but should we dismiss this simply on the basis that we ingest so many milligrammes of lead every day? Fairly large amounts of lead, ingested in conjunction with phosphate and other materials which would prevent its absorption, might be quite innocuous, whereas lead inhaled in very small concentrations could be quite harmful.

Barnes: The average concentration of lead in the air of Fleet Street in London, found in observations extending over twelve

* For further discussion of lead poisoning, see pp. 74–75.

months, was 3·2 μg lead per cubic metre (Waller, Commins and Lawther, 1965). This gives an average intake of 15 μg by inhalation for anyone spending 24 hours in the street. When lead is ingested it may get straight into the blood and thence to the brain, but we should remember that 1·5 mg of lead is already circulating in the blood of the unexposed adult.

Joyce: But surely whole body amounts *per se* cannot tell us anything. We need to know where a substance acts and in what concentration. The amounts of botulinum toxin or LSD needed to produce a dramatic effect are very small indeed. The justification for a meeting like this is to discuss techniques for predicting whether small amounts of potentially toxic substances will prove to be toxic without having to submit large numbers of people to the risk of toxicity.

Barnes: When the records of subjects with a history of a heavy occupational exposure to lead were studied, an increased incidence of death from cerebrovascular accidents was found (Dingwall-Fordyce and Lane, 1963). The men with smaller occupational exposure to lead did not show this.★

If one suspects that a substance is toxic in small amounts and is likely to be encountered by the general population, it is surely reasonable to begin by studying people with an above average exposure, and such groups are often found in certain occupations. For example, Laws, Curley and Biros (1967) studied 35 men in a group of subjects exposed to a concentration of DDT some 450 times as great as that to which the general population is exposed. No disease or increased absence from work due to sickness was found in the 35 men at "risk".

Albert: Professor Harris' presentation suggests that these results are not necessarily valid. If the incidence of a genetic predisposition is 1 in 5000, what help is a study of 35 subjects?

Harris: These frequencies vary a great deal. There is a classical story about atropinase in the rabbit. In any bunch of laboratory rabbits some have no significant atropinase activity while in the others the activity is quite high. The difference is inherited in quite a simple way. How this polymorphism is maintained I do not know. There is no atropinase in human serum, and I have often wondered what pharmacological properties of atropine would have been predicted if the pharmacology had

★ For further discussion of lead poisoning, see p. 188.

been worked out entirely on the rabbit and the results applied to man.

Barnes: Most laboratory animals are very insensitive to atropine, whereas human beings react violently to an overdose.

REFERENCES

BLACKWELL, B., and MARLEY, E. (1966). *Br. J. Pharmac. Chemother.*, **26**, 120–141.

BLACKWELL, B., MARLEY, E., PRICE, J., and TAYLOR, D. (1967). *Br. J. Psychiat. Chemother*, **113**, 349–365.

BONHAM CARTER, S., KAROUM, F., SANDLER, M., and YOUDIM, M. B. H. (1970). *Br. J. Pharmac.*, **39**, 202 P–203 P.

DINGWALL-FORDYCE, I., and LANE, R. E. (1963). *Br. J. ind. Med.*, **20**, 313–315.

FLATZ, G., SAENGUDOM, C., and SANGUANBHOKHAI, T. (1969). *Nature, Lond.*, **221**, 758–759.

HANINGTON, E. (1967). *Br. J. med.*, **2**, 550.

KATZ, D. (1953). *Animals and Men.* New translation by Steinberg, H., and Summerfield, A. Pelican edn. London: Penguin.

KOPIN, I. J. (1966). *Pharmac. Rev.*, **18**, 513.

LAWS, E. R., CURLEY, A., and BIROS, F. J. (1967). *Archs envir. Hlth*, **15**, 766–777.

RICHTER, C. P., HOLT, L. E., and BARELANE, B. (1938). *Am. J. Physiol.*, **122**, 734.

SANDLER, M., YOUDIM, M. B. H., SOUTHGATE, J., and HANINGTON, E. (1970). In *Background to Migraine (Proc. III Int. Migraine Symp.)*, pp. 104–115, ed. Cochrane, A. L. London: Heinemann.

SMITH, I., KELLOW, A. H., and HANINGTON, E. (1970). In *Background to Migraine (Proc. III Int. Migraine Symp.)*, pp. 120–126, ed. Cochrane, A. L. London: Heinemann.

WALLER, R. E., COMMINS, B. T., and LAWTHER, P. J. (1965). *Br. J. ind. Med.*, **22**, 128–138.

CHRONIC CENTRAL NERVOUS SYSTEM DAMAGE BY ENVIRONMENTAL AGENTS*

Roy E. Albert

Institute of Environmental Medicine, New York University Medical Center, New York

THE purpose of these remarks is to call attention to the possible importance of irreversible central nervous system (CNS) injury caused by exposure to environmental agents.

We first became concerned with this problem in a follow-up study of children who had received X-ray epilation of the scalp as treatment for ringworm of the scalp (tinea capitis). This form of treatment has been in general use on a world-wide scale since the first decade of this century. Its purpose is to remove all the scalp hair temporarily and painlessly to permit effective cleansing of the scalp. X-rays were administered in a highly standardized procedure which exposed the entire surface of the scalp. The dose given to the scalp was about 800 rads and that received by the brain very substantial, averaging 150 rads at the surface of the cortex and decreasing in the deeper parts of the brain to 50 rads at its base.

At our Institute 2400 children were irradiated between the years 1940–1958. After 1958 X-ray epilation was supplanted by treatment with the antibiotic griseofulvin. The average age of the treated population was 7 years with a range of 2 to 14 years. A control population of 1800 cases of tinea capitis, well-matched for age, sex and race, was not treated by X-ray epilation for various reasons during the same period. About 80 per cent of the cases in both treatment groups were located, the average length of time between treatment and location was 13 years. Information about their health was obtained by a simple questionnaire which in effect asked if there had been any treated illness after the ringworm infection. Diagnoses were obtained directly from the attending physician or medical institution.

The Chairman of this Study Group, in his opening remarks (p. 2), presented some of the data from this study; these indicated

* This presentation was contributed by Dr Albert after the meeting.

that there was a higher incidence of mental disease in the irradiated group. These results raised the question of whether mental disease produced by irradiation was an all-or-none response, or whether the irradiation injury occurred to a greater or lesser extent in most subjects in the irradiated group. We examined cases from both control and treatment groups for evidence of minor forms of mental illness. The examination consisted of a half-an-hour standardized interview by a psychiatrist and several psychological tests, the most important of which was the Minnesota Multi-phasic Personality Index (MMPI). The characterization of minor mental disability proved to be an extremely formidable problem for various reasons. It was difficult to obtain cooperation for an examination whose purpose had to be camouflaged, and only one quarter of the contacted cases actually submitted. This sampling bias probably accounted for the finding by psychiatric interview that only one half of the cases, regardless of treatment group, were free of some features of mental illness. I doubt if this high incidence can be ascribed to the rigours of life in New York City, but it was hardly surprising that differences between the irradiated and control groups were unimpressive. From an epidemiological standpoint the available techniques are poor for assessing minor degrees of mental disturbance. A single interview can at best give the psychiatrist only a general impression of the mental status of an individual. There were also considerable discrepancies between the results of the psychiatric interview and the psychological tests.

Radiation is not the only environmental factor implicated as a possible cause of CNS damage. Another example of such an agent is lead. Lead poisoning in children can produce irreparable brain damage with permanent mental retardation. The rising levels of lead in the environment, largely due to the combustion of gasoline containing lead, accounts for the increasing lead exposures in industrialized countries. Much more severe overexposures occur in slum children in several cities in the United States. The New York City Health Department Laboratory reports 600 to 900 children per year with elevated levels of lead in their blood. In one major New York City hospital, King's County Hospital, in the "lead belt" of Brooklyn, 4 per cent of the paediatric admissions are for lead poisoning. In dilapidated tenement buildings teething children, usually about the age of two years, are prone to eat flaking, lead-containing, wall paint. There is a very real possibility that the cases of lead poisoning represent only a tiny fraction of the number of slum children who ingest substantial amounts of lead paint. The question of whether chronic CNS impairment in large numbers of slum children could result from lead exposures which are acutely subtoxic is a social problem of chilling consequence.*

The two examples cited here indicate that the long-term CNS effects of environmental agents may be of importance, but it is also clear that the detection of subtle forms of impaired brain function is extremely difficult.

* For discussion see pp. 69–71.

DIETARY FACTORS AND SCHIZOPHRENIA

Seymour S. Kety

Department of Psychiatry, Harvard Medical School, Boston, Massachusetts

It is estimated that in the early years of this century as many as 10 per cent of the inmates of psychiatric hospitals in large regions of the United States and in many other parts of the world had been hospitalized because of the mental disturbances associated with pellagra. After the recognition of that condition as a vitamin deficiency and its successful prevention and treatment with nicotinic acid, a biochemical aetiology for one form of mental illness may be said to have been established. That substantial contribution seems to have served as a precedent for entertaining the possibility that other forms of mental illness, such as the disorders we call schizophrenia which are at present of obscure origin, may be due to a biochemical disturbance which may be genetic or environmental or, what has been most recently suggested, due to the operation of an environmental toxin or deficiency upon a genetically susceptible substrate. Certain characteristics of schizophrenic patients have made the evaluation of such hypotheses especially difficult.

DIETARY FACTORS AS ARTEFACTS OR IRRELEVANT VARIABLES IN SCHIZOPHRENIA

Most biological research in schizophrenia is carried out in patients with a long history of hospitalization in institutions where overcrowding is difficult to avoid and hygienic standards cannot always be maintained. It is easy to imagine the spread of chronic infections, especially of the digestive tract, among such patients. Even in the absence of previous or current infections, the development of a characteristic pattern of intestinal flora in a population of schizophrenic patients living together for long periods and fed from the same kitchen is a possibility that cannot be dismissed in interpreting what appear to be deviant metabolic pathways.

The variety and quality of the diet of the institutionalized schizophrenic is rarely comparable to that of the nonhospitalized normal control. In the acutely ill schizophrenic, the weeks or months of emotional turmoil which precede the recognition and diagnosis of the disorder are hardly conducive to a normal dietary intake. It is not unusual to find evidence of fairly severe vitamin or protein deficiencies among institutionalized schizophrenics (McDonald *et al.*, 1961). Horwitt (1953) found signs of liver dysfunction not unlike that which had been reported in schizophrenia, as a result of a diet containing border-line levels of protein. Nonspecific vitamin therapy accompanied by high protein and carbohydrate ingestion has been reported to reverse the impairment of hepatic function in schizophrenic patients (Horwitt *et al.*, 1948).

Even in institutions where the diet is adequate it is still far from offering a free choice. Evidence of thyroid dysfunction which had been attributed to schizophrenia was found to be associated with an institutional diet deficient in iodine and disappeared when iodized salt was added (Kelsey, Gullock and Kelsey, 1957). Aromatic amine metabolites thought to be associated with schizophrenia were later found to be of exogenous origin and closely correlated with the drinking of coffee (Mann and LaBrosse, 1959) or tea (J. R. Stabenau, C. R. Creveling and J. Daly, unpublished).

The phenothiazine drugs, in addition to their effectiveness and widespread use in schizophrenics, have numerous chromatogenic metabolites which continue to be excreted for weeks after the drugs are withdrawn (Closs, Wad and Ose, 1967) and have been confused with an amine metabolite which appeared to be characteristically associated with schizophrenia.

SOME DIETARY SUBSTANCES TO WHICH SPECIAL SIGNIFICANCE HAS
BEEN ATTACHED FOR THE AETIOLOGY OR TREATMENT
OF SCHIZOPHRENIA

Niacinamide and related substances

Reference has already been made to the highly specific use of nicotinic acid in relieving the mental and somatic symptoms of pellagra. In the ensuing years the acid or amide form of this vitamin has been tried nonspecifically in the treatment of a wide range of mental illness without spectacular success. One recent proposal for its use which has been widely promulgated has a rationale based upon the hypothesis first proposed by Harley-Mason in conjunction with Osmond and Smythies (1952): that one or more psychotoxic substances accumulated in schizo-phrenia as the result of biological transmethylation of normal metabolites. Hoffer and co-workers (1957) proposed that if this were so, large doses of a methyl acceptor should competitively divert the transmethylation and lower the levels of the hypothetical psychotoxic methylated metabolites. They administered large doses of nicotinic acid, nicotinamide or nicotinamide-adenine dinucleotide to schizophrenics and reported beneficial results. Controlled experiments which have attempted to confirm these findings have been successful in one trial using nicotinic acid (J. V. Ananth, T. A. Ban, H. E. Lehmann and J. Bennett, unpub-lished), but unsuccessful in two instances in which nicotinamide (S. D. McGrath, P. F. O'Brien, P. J. Power and J. R. Shea, un-published) or its adenine dinucleotide (Kline *et al.*, 1967) was administered. Studies in animals have given reason to question the efficacy of nicotinamide as a methyl acceptor in the brain, on the basis of its inability to lower the brain levels of S-adeno-sylmethionine (Baldessarini, 1966).

Ascorbic acid

In 1957 Akerfeldt proposed a blood test for schizophrenia based upon the apparent ability of the serum of such patients to oxidize N,N-dimethyl-p-phenylenediamine (DPP) more rapidly than can the serum of normal people. Also adrenaline has been reported to oxidize the serum of schizophrenics more rapidly than does normal serum (Leach and Heath, 1956). Two serum con-stituents are involved in both reactions: ceruloplasmin which acts as an oxidase for many substrates including DPP and adrena-line, and ascorbic acid which antagonizes the process. Several workers found that the ceruloplasmin was elevated in the serum of schizophrenics, while others found a depressed level of ascorbic acid. Akerfeldt noted that these levels did not rise normally after ascorbic acid loading, which suggests an abnormality in the metabolism of that vitamin.

McDonald and co-workers (1961) were unable to confirm either elevation of ceruloplasmin or depression of ascorbic acid in a group of schizophrenics who had been maintained on a good diet, and they failed to observe greater than normal oxidation of either substrate in their sera. In a series of well-conducted studies they demonstrated that institutionalized schizophrenics with initially low serum ascorbic acid levels responded normally to ascorbic acid loading, while normal volunteers on ascorbate deficient diets showed a reduction in the concentration of serum ascorbic acid. The oxidation of DPP was highly correlated with the serum ascorbic acid at the time of the test and with the amounts of vitamin C ingested, and not correlated with the presence or absence of schizophrenia.

"Megadose" vitamin therapies

Pauling (1968) raised the possibility that there is a much wider variance in the requirements for vitamins and other essential dietary components than has been suspected and that some individuals may suffer from dietary deficiencies even while ingesting what is considered to be the "minimum daily requirement". He has further suggested that some forms of mental illness may be manifestations of such deficiencies. Such hypotheses are certainly tenable and heuristic, and studies of the metabolism of certain vitamins in schizophrenic patients have been undertaken at Pauling's laboratory. On the assumption that such hypotheses may be valid and that large doses of certain normal dietary ingredients cannot be harmful, some attempts are being made to treat various forms of mental illness with so-called "megadose vitamin therapy". The most extensive attempt is one which has been organized by Rimland on childhood psychoses. Specially prepared dietary supplements containing iron, choline, inositol, vitamins B_1, B_2, B_6, B_{12}, folic acid, nicotinamide, pantothenic acid, para-aminobenzoic acid, biotin, and vitamin C are administered daily for several months to a large number of mentally ill children under the care of their own physicians. The physicians and the parents of the children participating in the study have been given a prospectus describing the treatment and citing in the most enthusiastic terms the beneficial effects achieved in a number of individual cases. A detailed diagnostic questionnaire completed before treatment begins is analyzed by a computer to identify, within the total population, smaller subgroups of children homogeneous as to symptomatology; the extent of behavioural change in each homogeneous cluster will be compared by analysis of variance to determine whether there are significant differences in improvement between subgroups. The criteria for evaluating the treatment of efficacy between subgroups will be: reports from parents, reports from the physician, and the percentage of families reordering the vitamins. Rimland indicates that "if the subgroups differ significantly in their response to the treatment, we will know not only that the treatment works, but also which children in any new group may be expected to benefit". Since the conventional double-blind procedure is not being used and ample opportunity is being given for the operation of a "halo" effect, it would be surprising if apparent therapeutic benefit was not found in many of the patients and in some of the numerous subgroups. A very sophisticated statistical analysis will be required to rule out the placebo effect and to adequately account for "chance" results, otherwise an erroneous conclusion, that the particular therapy is of benefit in one or more types of childhood psychosis, may be drawn.

Cereal grain products

Some reports have indicated an increased frequency of coeliac disease in schizophrenics and some similarities in symptomatology between the two disorders. Also, the role of gluten-containing cereals in the pathogenesis of coeliac disease has been recognized. These findings led Dohan (1966) to suggest that the ingestion of such cereals may play a role in the pathogenesis of schizophrenia. He noted a decreased incidence of schizophrenia in Scandinavian countries during World War II, and found that this was associated with a decrease in wheat consumption; there was a highly significant correlation between hospital admissions for schizophrenia and wheat consumption in these countries and in Canada and the United States. Dohan's observations in patients, including those with coeliac disease and a remitted schizophrenic patient exhibiting an acute hallucinatory psychosis following the ingestion of rice or gluten, support this hypothesis. He and his associates (Dohan et al., 1969) conducted a double-blind study of 102 schizophrenic patients randomly assigned to a high cereal diet, a milk- and cereal-free diet, and a cereal-free diet to which wheat gluten was secretly added. Significantly greater improvement occurred in the patients who were on the cereal-free diet than occurred in those assigned to diets which contained gluten. Sixty-two per cent of 47 patients on a cereal-free diet, compared to 36 per cent of 55 on the high cereal diet were released from the locked ward before the end of the median stay ($P = 0 \cdot 009$) and during the period of assignment to the cereal-free-plus-gluten diet the rate of improvement did not differ from that of the patients on the high cereal diet. This hypothesis and the controlled study which supports it deserve further exploration, but so far no independent attempt has been made to replicate it.

Methionine

Some recent evidence is compatible with the possibility that this amino acid may be involved in the pathogenesis of schizophrenia. If the abnormalities in biological transmethylation or the accumulation of methylated metabolites were important in the aetiology of schizophrenia, this amino acid, which is the precursor of S-adenosylmethionine the methyl donor primarily involved in transmethylation, would be an important link in the sequence. Pollin, Cardon and Kety (1961) attempted to test the transmethylation hypothesis in schizophrenia by administering large doses of L-methionine (20 g per day) with the consent of the patients and their families. To favour the accumulation of methylated amines, should they occur, a monoamine oxidase inhibitor was also administered to the patients. Four of the twelve patients exhibited an acute psychotic exacerbation after the first few days of methionine administration. This effect of methionine has now been confirmed in independent studies (Alexander et al., 1963; Brune and Himwich, 1962, 1963; Haydu et al., 1965). In one such study it was also demonstrated that betaine, a methyl donor unrelated to methionine, exerted a similar effect. Large doses of methionine fed to animals have been shown to elevate significantly the levels of S-adenosyl-methionine in the brain (Baldessarini, 1966) and an enzymic activity has been found in mammalian tissue (Axelrod, 1961) which catalyses the N-methylation of tryptamine to form the hallucinogen, dimethyltryptamine. Although these observations suggest that possibly methionine acts in schizophrenia by favouring biological transmethylation and intensifying the pathogenic process in the disorder, that action has not been established nor have a number of alternative hypotheses been ruled out. It has not been possible to demonstrate in man that the methylation of catecholamines is favoured by methionine administration but, more important, the crucial question about the nature of the induced psychosis has not been resolved. Although the original observers were impressed by the intensification of idiosyncratic and schizophrenic symptoms caused by methionine in the individual patients, it is equally possible that the methionine produced a toxic psychosis or a schizophrenic reaction to toxic symptoms in these patients. Large doses of methionine have been reported to induce psychotic manifestations in non-schizo-phrenic patients, especially individuals with hepatic insufficiency, but the manifestations here are more typically those of a toxic psychosis.

The differentiation between toxic psychosis and schizophrenia requires careful thought and further exploration not only in interpreting the effects of methionine, but also because of its bearing on the whole question of whether schizophrenia or some of its forms may be caused by nutritional deficits or environ-mental toxins. It has been traditional in psychiatry to separate clearly the manifestations of the toxic or somatic psychoses from those of schizophrenia, and indeed such a differentiation is relatively clear to most experienced psychiatrists. On the other hand, it may be argued that those differentiations hold best where they merely confirm other evidence of the nature of the psychosis in question. The acute psychosis induced by a number of psy-chotomimetic drugs cannot be readily distinguished from the acute psychotic episode which heralds the more persistent mani-festations of schizophrenia. It is not unusual to find that patients who have been diagnosed and treated as typical schizophrenics in the best psychiatric institutions were later found to have been suffering from a toxic symptomatic psychosis. This is especially true for chronic amphetamine psychosis and for some of the psychoses associated with temporal lobe lesions, both of which bear striking similarities to schizophrenia.

Recent evidence (Kety et al., 1969) indicates that genetic factors operate significantly in the aetiology of schizophrenia but does not rule out, and in fact may even imply, that as yet unspecified environmental factors are also required. Although the evidence which has been briefly reviewed hardly implicates any nutritional or environmental chemical factor as being of aetiological significance in any subgroup of schizophrenia, the possibility that this may be so is still a lively one and merits, perhaps, more attention than it has been accorded.

It cannot be emphasized too often that the human brain and human behaviour are far more complex than any other structure or function of which we are aware. So much of human behaviour is dependent on the circuitry of the brain, and so much more on the information derived from idiosyncratic life experience which is stored within it, that a simple chemical cause or explanation of most mental illnesses is not likely. Fortunately, it is not necessary to postulate that chemistry will have all of the answers to justify continued search for the biochemical variables which undoubtedly play a significant role in the mediation or modulation of human behaviour.

SUMMARY

Dietary factors have often been implicated by means of hypotheses or by data as aetiological factors in schizophrenia. The well-established association between certain nutritional deficiencies and psychosis, best illustrated, perhaps, by pellagra, lends some credence to the possibility that a mental disorder of unknown aetiology may also have a nutritional basis. On the other hand, many changes which are not aetiological, but which depend upon the chronicity of the disorder, the types of behaviour and the institutionalization and treatment often associated with schizophrenia, impose special problems on the design of experiments and the interpretation of results. An attempt is made to review the evidence which links certain nutritional factors, i.e. vitamins such as nicotinic acid and ascorbic acid, food stuffs such as cereals and protein constituents such as methionine or aromatic amino acids, to the schizophrenic disorders either aetiologically or therapeutically.

REFERENCES

AKERFELDT, S. (1957). *Science*, **125**, 117–119.
ALEXANDER, F., CURTIS, G. C., SPRINCE, H., and CROSLEY, A. P. (1963). *J. nerv. ment. Dis.*, **137**, 135–142.
AXELROD, J. (1961). *Science*, **134**, 343.

BALDESSARINI, R. J. (1966). *Biochem. Pharmac.*, **15**, 741–748.

BRUNE, G. G., and HIMWICH, H. E. (1962). *J. nerv. ment. Dis.*, **134**, 447–450.

BRUNE, G. G., and HIMWICH, H. E. (1963). *Recent Adv. Biol. Psychiat.*, **5**, 144–160.

CLOSS, K., WAD, N., and OSE, E. (1967). *Nature, Lond.*, **214**, 483.

DOHAN, F. C. (1966). *Acta psychiat. scand.*, **42**, 125–152.

DOHAN, F. C., GRASBERGER, J. C., LOWELL, F. M., JOHNSTON, H. T., and ARBEGAST, A. W. (1969). *Br. J. Psychiat.*, **115**, 595–596.

HAYDU, G. G., DHRYMIOTIS, A., KORENYI, C., and GOLDSCHMIDT, L. (1965). *Am. J. Psychiat.*, **122**, 560–564.

HOFFER, A., OSMOND, H., CALLBECK, M. J., and KAHAN, I. (1957). *J. clin. exp. Psychopath.*, **18**, 131–158.

HORWITT, M. K. (1953). In *Nutrition Symposium Series*, No. 7, pp. 67–83, ed. Alexander, W. F. *et al.* New York: National Vitamin Foundation.

HORWITT, M. K., LIEBERT, E., KREISLER, O., and WITTMAN, P. (1948). In *National Research Council Bulletin*, No. 116. Washington: National Academy of Sciences.

KELSEY, F. O., GULLOCK, A. H., and KELSEY, F. E. (1957). *A.M.A. Archs Neurol. Psychiatry*, **77**, 543–548.

KETY, S. S., ROSENTHAL, D., WENDER, P. H., and SCHULSINGER, F. (1969). *J. Psychiat. Res.*, **6**, suppl., 345–362.

KLINE, N. S., BARCLAY, G. L., COLE, J. O., ESSER, A. H., LEHMANN, H., and WITTENBORN, J. R. (1967). *Br. J. Psychiat.*, **113**, 731–742.

LEACH, B. E., and HEATH, R. G. (1956). *A.M.A. Archs Neurol. Psychiatry*, **76**, 444–450.

MCDONALD, R. K., WEISE, V. K., EVANS, F. T., and PATRICK, R. W. (1961). In *Chemical Pathology of the Nervous System* (Proc. III Int. neurochem. Symp., Strasbourg, 1958), pp. 404–413, ed. Folch-Pi, J. Oxford: Pergamon.

MANN, J. D., and LABROSSE, E. H. (1959). *Archs gen. Psychiat.*, **1**, 547–551.

OSMOND, H., and SMYTHIES, J. (1952). *J. ment. Sci.*, **98**, 309–315.

PAULING, L. (1968). *Science*, **160**, 265–271.

POLLIN, W., CARDON, P. V., and KETY, S. S. (1961). *Science*, **133**, 104–105.

DISCUSSION

Boyland: Have the effects you have described only been produced with large doses of methionine?

Kety: As L-methionine did not produce these effects in the same dosage I suspect that large doses would be needed.

Boyland: The addition of amino acids to food has been suggested as a treatment for schizophrenia but the quantities would not approach 20 grammes a day.

Lewis: Twenty years ago glutamic acid was reported to produce an improvement in the intelligence level of mentally retarded children, especially mongols, but the claim was not confirmed.

Boyland: Monosodium glutamate is frequently added to food and probably produces behavioural effects.

Brimblecombe: I have always been impressed by your work with methionine, Professor Kety, and by Himwick and his colleagues' studies with betaine (see Brune, 1965). If one allies this to the methylation hypothesis of Osmond and Smythies (1952) we have an attractive hypothesis suggesting that an endogenously produced substance may be responsible for schizophrenia, especially when one considers that methylated derivatives of naturally occurring substances are hallucinogenic. Do I understand that you are not very enthusiastic about this?

Kety: I am open-minded. The betaine story, which seemed to be an independent and unusual confirmation of this hypothesis, is not as compelling as it seemed since it has been found that betaine elevates the levels of methionine in the body. We were never able to establish that methionine really intensified schizophrenia, although in individual patients there was an intensification of particular psychotic symptoms. I doubt whether normal individuals given 20 grammes of methionine daily would become psychotic. It is difficult to designate the effects of a toxic psychosis in a schizophrenic patient. It might lead to an intensification of symptoms already present, but by a circuitous psychological route rather than by a biochemical one.

King: I am interested in the comparison you made between drug-induced and naturally occurring psychosis. Hollister (1968) is not as convinced as you are about this parallel. One of the examples he cites is that most chemically induced psychoses produce visual hallucinations, whereas the drug-induced psychoses give rise to auditory phenomena.

Kety: Traditional psychiatry has made a distinction between toxic or symptomatic psychosis and schizophrenia. I think that it is possible to differentiate the two by such factors as auditory or visual hallucinations, the presence of clear consciousness or delirium and so on. One of the important arguments against the notion that schizophrenia is caused by a chemical substance is that it is so difficult to produce by chemical agents a syndrome indistinguishable from schizophrenia; most chemical agents produce a syndrome typical of a toxic psychosis. But much of the differentiation between a toxic or natural psychosis is based on the history. I wanted to indicate that occasionally, but often enough to raise a question, a drug-induced toxic psychosis may be indistinguishable from an acute schizophrenic reaction which eventually leads to schizophrenia. The first symptoms of schizophrenia often resemble the toxic psychosis which, as Dr Hollister correctly points out, is quite different from schizophrenia. A patient who is diagnosed as schizophrenic may subsequently be found to be suffering from chronic amphetamine toxicity or temporal lobe epilepsy. We should be aware that it is not always easy to separate the toxic psychoses from schizophrenia.

Harris: Is there any evidence for an increased incidence of psychotic episodes in patients with homocystinuria?

Kety: Yes. Mental retardation is common in homocystinurics; but a high incidence of schizophrenia has been described in one or two families of patients with homocystinuria (Himwick, Kety and Smythies, 1967). This could be a coincidence.

Harris: Most of the patients with schizophrenia in these families presumably have not got overt homocystinuria.

Kety: That is correct.

Sandler: We have to consider a number of other possible ways, both direct and indirect, by which dietary factors could, potentially, modify behaviour. Food spoilage by hallucinogenic fungi is one possibility; the precedent for this is ergotism. But even our normal diet needs reassessment; nutmeg, for example, is known to contain both a hallucinogenic alkaloid, myristicin (Weiss, 1960), and a monoamine oxidase inhibitor (Truitt, Duritz and Ebersberger, 1963). The intestinal flora are another factor external to the body's economy which can both chemically modify dietary constituents and alter the body's response to them. Germ-free chicks have a higher hepatic monoamine oxidase activity than controls (Phillips *et al.*, 1962). Oral L-dopa therapy is now being widely used in the treatment of Parkinsonism (for review, see Calne and Sandler, 1970). A small amount of this drug undergoes *p*-dehydroxylation (Calne *et al.*, 1969), a transformation mediated by the action of the intestinal flora (Sandler *et al.*, 1969). It is not yet known to what extent *m*-hydroxylated products, particularly *m*-tyrosine which is known to possess powerful pharmacological effects (Mitoma *et al.*, 1957; Blaschko and Chruściel, 1960; Carlsson and Lindqvist, 1969), contribute to the clinical response to such treatment.

Kety: These are important possibilities. But it would be hard to imagine a population in our culture eating spoiled food regularly and becoming chronically schizophrenic.

Steinberg: There are various forms of schizophrenia. We may be forced to look for multiple biochemical predisposing factors just as we recognize that many different combinations of symptoms can occur.

Kety: Although various pharmacological agents cause these sorts of illnesses it is difficult to find any agent which produces the cardinal features of classical schizophrenia. Nitrous oxide gives rise to auditory hallucinations but also causes severe delirium. It is not so easy to find a substance which will produce auditory hallucinations on a clear sensorium.

Weiskrantz: Nevertheless, as you have said, the acute phases of schizophrenia and a pharmacologically induced psychosis may have similar features. Once the illness has become chronic, one does not know what sort of positive feedback loops exist. For example, it was recently claimed that schizophrenics are relatively insensitive to non-verbal cues of communication. A subject who is unresponsive to certain kinds of stimulation for many years is in a unique state of sensory deprivation, and this will produce a complex clinical picture that it would be difficult to mimic with any chemical agent. To mimic chronic schizophrenia one would have to use continuous doses of the chemical over many years.

Kety: That particular assumption runs counter to many of the hypotheses and observations about schizophrenia. The schizophrenic is, if anything, more open to sensory stimuli, although less able to attend to a particular stimulus, than is the normal subject. This difference was well demonstrated when a chief resident in psychiatry at Johns Hopkins University was giving psychotherapy to a schizophrenic patient. At the end of the session the patient said: "One of the things that disturbed me in the course of this session was the baby crying". The resident had not heard a baby crying, but she replayed the tape of the session and throughout it there was a cat meowing.

Weiskrantz: My point still stands. I do not necessarily want to endorse the claim that schizophrenics are insensitive to non-verbal cues—facial expression, posture and so on. I merely used this claim to illustrate my general point that the occurrence of this disease subsequently produces a particular environment

4

for the patient, and that this is difficult to mimic by any artificial means.

REFERENCES

BLASCHKO, H., and CHRUŚCIEL, T. L. (1960). *J. Physiol. Lond.*, **151**, 272–284.

BRUNE, G. G. (1965). In *Horizons in Neuropsychopharmacology* [Progress in Brain Research, **16**] pp. 81–96, ed. Himwick, W. A., and Scháde, J. P. Amsterdam: Elsevier.

CALNE, D. B., KAROUM, F., RUTHVEN, C. R. J., and SANDLER, M. (1969). *Br. J. Pharmac.*, **37**, 57.

CALNE, D. B., and SANDLER, M. (1970). *Nature, Lond.*, **226**, 21–24.

CARLSSON, A., and LINDQVIST, M. (1969). *Eur. J. Pharmac.*, **2**, 187.

HIMWICK, H. E., KETY, S. S., and SMYTHIES, J. R. (eds) (1967). *Amines and Schizophrenia*, p. 265. Harmondsworth: Penguin Books.

HOLLISTER, L. E. (1968). *Chemical Psychoses: LSD and Related Drugs.* Springfield: Thomas.

MITOMA, C., POSNER, H. S., BOGDANSKI, D. F., and UDENFRIEND, S. (1957). *J. Pharmac. exp. Ther.*, **120**, 188.

OSMOND, H., and SMYTHIES, J. (1952). *J. ment. Sci.*, **98**, 309–315.

PHILLIPS, A. W., NEWCOMB, H. R., RUPP, F. A., and LACHAPELLE, R. (1962). *J. Nutr.*, **76**, 119.

SANDLER, M., KAROUM, F., RUTHVEN, C. R. J., and CALNE, D. B. (1969). *Science*, **166**, 1417.

TRUITT, E. B., JR., DURITZ, G., and EBERSBERGER, E. M. (1963). *Proc. Soc. exp. Biol. Med.*, **112**, 647.

WEISS, G. (1960). *Psychiat. Q.*, **34**, 346.

EFFECTS OF DRUG-DRUG AND DRUG-FOOD INTER-ACTION ON DRUG LEVELS AND PERFORMANCE IN MAN

A. H. BECKETT

Department of Pharmacy, Chelsea College of Science and Technology, London

BEHAVIOUR can be influenced by many factors, many of which may be deliberately or inadvertently altered by changes in the chemical environment of the individual. Probably most of the manifestations of activity in man will finally be described in biochemical terms even though at present our knowledge of the complex biochemical inter-relationships is superficial and fragmentary. There is convincing evidence for chemical trans-mission in nervous activity in peripheral tissues and rapidly increasing evidence for chemical transmission in the central nervous system (CNS). Faulty functioning of the brain might result from an imbalance of local enzyme systems or from a general biochemical deficiency. According to recent assessment, one per cent to three per cent of the population of the world is mentally retarded; in economically advanced populations, 10 per cent of the cases result from known inborn biochemical factors (WHO, 1969). However, many enzymes responsible for hereditary abnormalities have still to be identified.

Man is being presented internally and externally with in-creasing numbers of foreign compounds in foods, medicines, solvents, detergents, cosmetics, the atmosphere, etc., and these can interact with the integrated balance of endogenous enzymes and substrates and chemical transmitters in ways which will affect this balance and thus influence his behaviour.

The purpose of this paper is to indicate ways in which foreign compounds can interact chemically and biochemically in man and thus indirectly affect his behaviour.

Enhancement of enzyme activity

Many chemicals and drugs in the environment of man stimu-late hepatic enzyme activity and to a lesser extent other enzyme

activities in animals. Usually enzymic oxidative reactions are
increased first, but then the effect spreads to reducing, hydrolysing
and conjugating enzymes. Although, in general, increases
in enzymic actions tend to lead to quicker elimination of foreign
compounds from the body and to faster production of metabolites
which are less toxic than their parent molecules, there are excep-
tions. Chemicals which may be present as trace residues in food
such as polycyclic hydrocarbons, as well as many drugs, possess
these enzyme stimulating properties (see Table I) (Remmer,
1969). Enzyme stimulation by foreign compounds also occurs

TABLE I

SUBSTANCES STIMULATING THE ACTIVITY OF DRUG–METABOLIZING ENZYMES
IN ANIMALS

Pharmacological action	Substances tested as enzyme stimulators	Effect
Anaesthetic gases	Nitrous oxide	+
	Ether	+
	Chloroform	+
Hypnotics and sedatives	Urethane	+
	Carbromal	+ +
	Barbiturates	+ + +
	Pyridione	+ +
	Methyprylone	+ +
	Glutethimide	+ + +
	Ethanol	+
	Chloral hydrate	+
	Chlorbutanol	+
	Chloralose	+/−
Anticonvulsants	Diphenylhydantoin	+ +
	Methylphenylethylhydantoin	+ +
	Paramethadione	+ +
	Primidone	+ +
Tranquillizers	Chlorpromazine	+ +
	Triflupromazine	+ +
	Chlordiazepoxide	+
	Hydroxyzine	+
Antalgics	Phenylbutazone	+ + +
	Phenazone	+ +

Muscle relaxants	Mephenesin	+
	Meprobamate	+ +
	Phenaglycodol	+ + +
	Carisoprodol	+
Antihistaminics	Orphenadrine	+ +
	Diphenhydramine	+ +
	Chlorcyclizine	+ +
Central nervous system stimulants	Nikethamide	+ + +
	Bemegride	+ +
Antidepressants	Imipramine	+ +
	Iproniazid	+ +
Hypoglycaemic agents	Tolbutamide	+ + +
	Chlorpropamide	+ +
	Carbutamide	+ +
Inhibitors of cholesterol	Triparanol	+ +
	SKF-525A	+ +
Steroids	Nortestosterone	+
	Norethandrolone	+
	Norethynodrel	+
Insecticides	Chlordane	+ + + +
	DDT	+ + + +
	α- and γ-Hexachlorcyclohexane	+ + + +
	Dieldrin	+ + +
	Aldrin	+ + +
	Heptachlor	+ + +
	Heptachlor epoxide	+ +
Carcinogenic polycyclic hydrocarbons	3-Methylcholanthrene	+ + +
	3,4-Benzpyrene	+ + +
	1,2,5, 6-Dibenzanthracene	+

(After H. Remmer)

in man (Table II) but so far the examples are not so numerous as the confirmed examples in animals (Prescott, 1969). Insecticides, polycyclic hydrocarbons in smoke, and drugs have been shown to stimulate the metabolism of drugs, carcinogens and steroidal hormones in man (Table II) (Conney, 1969).

Cigarette smoking results in enhanced hydroxylation by the human placenta of the polycyclic aromatic hydrocarbon 3,4-benzpyrene present in cigarette smoke (Table III); no detectable benzpyrene hydroxylase activity was observed in human placentas

TABLE II

ENZYME INDUCTION IN MAN

Stimulator	*Enhanced metabolism*
Phenobarbitone and other barbiturates	Coumarin anticoagulants
	Diphenylhydantoin
	Griseofulvin
	Digitoxin
	Dipyrone
	Cortisol
	Testosterone
	Bilirubin
Glutethimide	Glutethimide
	Warfarin
	Dipyrone
Phenylbutazone	Aminopyrine
	Cortisol
Chloral hydrate	Bishydroxycoumarin
Meprobamate	Meprobamate
Ethanol	Pentobarbitone
	Tolbutamide
Diethylnicotinamide (Coramine)	Bilirubin
Diphenylhydantoin	Cortisol
o,p'-DDD	Cortisol
Cigarette smoke	3, 4-Benzpyrene
	3-Methyl-4-monomethyl-aminoazobenzene
	Nicotine
DDT, lindane	Antipyrine

obtained after childbirth from thirty non-smokers, but this enzyme activity was found in the placentas obtained from thirty women who smoked 10 to 40 cigarettes per day (Welch et al., 1969). The variability in benzpyrene hydroxylating activity in the placentas of different individuals smoking different numbers of cigarettes daily may indicate different individual inducibility of the enzymes. Also very much greater N-demethyl-ase activity was found in the placentas from cigarette smokers

TABLE III

EFFECT OF CIGARETTE SMOKING ON BENZPYRENE HYDROXYLASE ACTIVITY IN THE HUMAN PLACENTA

Patient	Cigarettes smoked daily during pregnancy	Hydroxybenzpyrene formed by placenta ($ng/g/h$)
S.I.	0	0
S.K.	0	0
D.L.	0	0
F.L.	0	0
M.C.	0	0
H.D.	0	0
C.G.	20	643
R.S.	20–30	826
A.T.	20	1,269
J.K.	20	1,317
C.J.	20	4,289
D.A.	20	15,181
M.N.	15–20	17,100
H.B.	40	23,205

Homogenate equivalent to 100 mg of placenta was incubated with 50 μg of benzpyrene and an NADPH-generating system for 15 min. Values of 0 for enzyme activity represent < 100 ng of hydroxybenzpyrene formed per g of placenta per h which is the lower limit of the sensitivity of the method.

than those from non-smokers (Table IV). Research into the metabolism of nicotine and other tobacco alkaloids has been facilitated by making human urine acidic to minimize kidney tubular absorption of bases; under these conditions, the excretion

TABLE IV

EFFECT OF CIGARETTE SMOKING ON AMINOAZO DYE N-DEMETHYLASE ACTIVITY IN HUMAN PLACENTA

Subjects	Number of subjects	3-Methyl-AB formed ($μg/g/h$)
Non-smokers	17	< 1
Smokers	17	6 (1–21)

Homogenate equivalent to 400 mg of placenta was incubated with 150 μg of 3-methyl-4-monomethylaminoazobenzene for 30 min in the presence of an NADPH-generating system. Formation of 3-methyl-4-aminoazobenzene (3-methyl-AB) was measured. The average and range are given.

of bases shows only slight intra-subject variations. Also, as in the case of amphetamine, there is a direct relationship between rate of excretion and plasma concentration in man with acidic (pH 4·8 to 5·0) urine, but not when the pH of the urine fluctuates (Fig. 1) (Beckett, Salmon and Mitchard, 1969). The kinetics of metabolism can be established under controlled conditions and

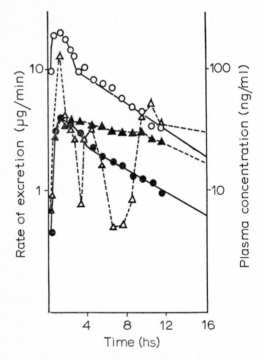

Fig. 1. Urinary excretion and plasma concentration of amphetamine after oral administration of 15 mg [14C]amphetamine sulphate while under conditions of acid-controlled and fluctuating urinary pH. Subject R.B.

O——O : Rate of excretion } Under conditions of
●——● : Plasma concentration } controlled urinary } pH.

△ - - - - - △ : Rate of excretion } Under conditions of
▲ - - - - - ▲ : Plasma concentration } fluctuating urinary } pH.

analogue computer techniques used to predict urinary excretion of a base under fluctuating urinary pH (see Fig. 2). Thus most of the metabolism by different subjects and of different alkaloids can be determined from urine data (see Figs. 3, 4, 5). Female non-smokers excrete more nicotine unchanged than do male non-smokers. Female smokers excrete less nicotine than female non-smokers, indicating that possibly smoking can increase the metabolism of nicotine (Fig. 4). From experience to date, male smokers may be divided into two groups, namely: those who excrete less nicotine than do non-smokers but excrete similar amounts of cotinine (major metabolite of nicotine), and those who excrete similar amounts of nicotine as non-smokers

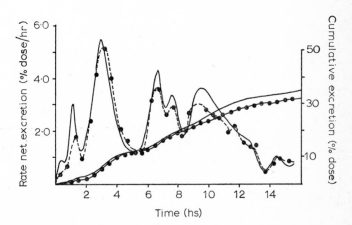

————: Computer predictions. —●—: Cumulative excretion.
---●---: Actual rates of excretion.

FIG. 2. A comparison of computer predicted and actual rates of excretion and cumulative excretion of amphetamine after oral administration of 15 mg D(+)-amphetamine sulphate in solution (subject 1).

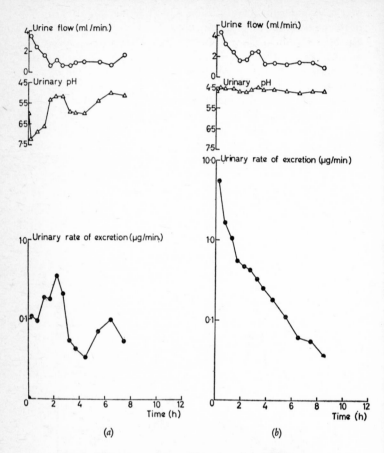

FIG. 3a. Urinary excretion of nicotine after the intravenous administration of 3·07 mg (−)-nicotine hydrogen (+)-tartrate under conditions of fluctuating urinary pH. Subject D.T.

FIG. 3b. Urinary excretion of nicotine after the intravenous administration of 3·07 mg (−)-nicotine hydrogen (+)-tartrate under conditions of acidic urinary pH. Subject D.T.

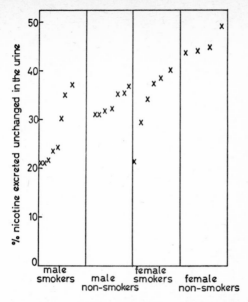

FIG. 4. Distribution of urinary nicotine recoveries in male and female smokers and non-smokers after intravenous administration of $3 \cdot 07$ mg $(-)$-nicotine hydrogen $(+)$-tartrate under conditions of acidic urinary pH.

(Fig. 4) but have three to five times enhancement of cotinine excretion (Beckett *et al.*, 1970).

Detailed studies of the metabolism of alcohol in man under controlled conditions give reproducible results of metabolic rates (e.g. Fig. 7 ; regular heavy alcohol drinkers are able to metabolize alcohol faster than moderate and occasional drinkers (Fig. 6) (Beckett *et al.*, 1970). Heavy drinkers are also known to have an enhanced metabolism of phenobarbitone (Rubin and Lieber, 1968) and tolbutamide (Kater, Tobon and Iber, 1969).

The workers in a pesticide factory exposed to the pesticide DDT and lindane are reported to metabolize the drug, antipyrine faster than a controlled population; probably these workers will therefore metabolize other foreign compounds faster than does the general population (Kolmodin, Azarnoff and Sjöqvist, 1969).

98   A. H. BECKETT

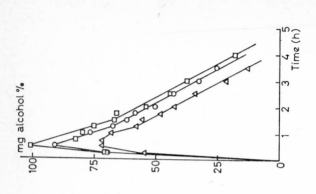

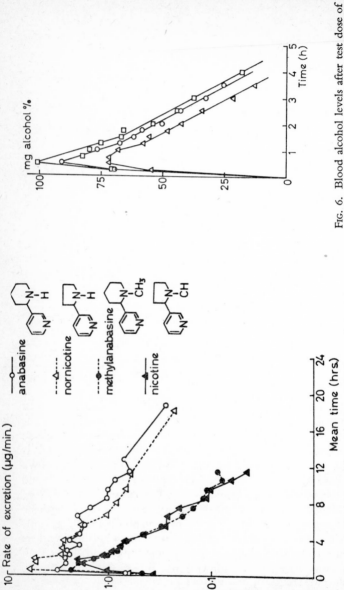

FIG. 5. Comparison of the urinary excretion rates of nicotine, nornicotine, methylanabasine and anabasine after an oral dose of 2 mg base. Male non-smoker, acidic urinary conditions.

FIG. 6. Blood alcohol levels after test dose of two double whiskies. Three determinations in one moderate drinker. Subject A.U. Metabolic rate≡19·5 mg per cent per hour.

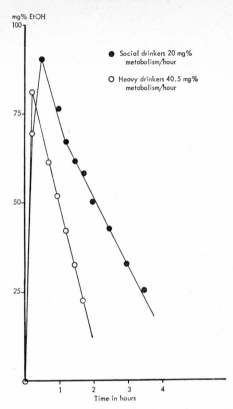

FIG. 7. Rate of alcohol metabolism by social and heavy
drinkers.

Prolonged treatment of epileptic patients with phenobarbitone increases the metabolism of diphenylhydantoin (Table V) (Cucinell *et al.*, 1965). The treatment of patients with barbiturates or phenylbutazone alters the relative importance of different routes of steroid metabolism (Conney, 1969), for example, the metabolism of cortisol to 6β-hydroxycortisol (normally a minor metabolite) is stimulated (Fig. 8). The chronic administration of N-phenylbarbital alters the metabolism of testosterone in man; increased excretion of more polar metabolites and decreased urinary excretion of androsterone and etiocholanolone results.

TABLE V

EFFECT OF PHENOBARBITONE ADMINISTRATION ON PLASMA LEVELS OF
DIPHENYLHYDANTOIN IN MAN

Drug treatment	No. of subjects	Plasma level of diphenylhydantoin (mg/l)
Diphenylhydantoin (300 mg)	10	$11 \cdot 4 \pm 1 \cdot 6$ (S.E.M.)
Diphenylhydantoin (300 mg) + Phenobarbitone (120 mg)	9	$3 \cdot 5 \pm 0 \cdot 7$ (S.E.M.)

Epileptic patients received drugs chronically for at least two months.

The above examples of stimulation of metabolism in man by foreign compounds, and the numerous examples in animals in which the metabolism of foreign compounds and endogenous materials including hormones is stimulated, indicate the need for extensive research in man in this field, since the circulating levels of hormones may well be affected by the foreign compounds introduced intentionally or inadvertently into his body from his environment.

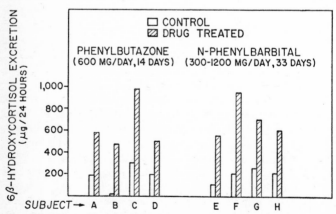

Fig. 8. Stimulatory effect of phenylbutazone and N-phenyl-barbital on the urinary excretion of 6β-hydroxycortisol in man.

INHIBITION OF ENZYME ACTIVITY

Some foreign compounds introduced into animals are known to inhibit metabolism by microsomal enzymes (Prescott, 1969), e.g. SKF 525A, analgesics, steroids, hormones and tranquillizers but, as in the case of enzyme stimulation, the established examples in man are relatively few.

The *p*-hydroxylation of the anticonvulsant phenytoin is reduced in man by the presence of phenylbutazone, isoniazid, dicoumarol, *p*-aminosalicylic acid and sulphaphenazole. Methylphenidate in man probably reduces the rate of metabolism of phenobarbitone, primidone, phenytoin and ethylbiscoumacetate. Probably steroids used in oral contraceptives will inhibit the metabolism of foreign compounds in women since urinary excretion of unchanged pethidine and promazine is increased in pregnancy and in women taking oral contraceptives (Crawford and Rudofsky, 1966). Hydrocortisone inhibited the metabolism of nortriptyline in a patient who had taken an overdose of the latter compound.

Some foreign compounds inhibit monoamine oxidases (MAO inhibitors) in animals and man and so reduce the rate of metabolism of many endogenous and exogenous amines. Their use to treat depression results from their indirect stimulant action which is considered to be due to their inhibiting monoamine oxidases and thus allowing the accumulation of endogenous catecholamines including noradrenaline and serotonin in brain tissue (Todd, 1967). The MAO inhibitors interfere with the metabolism of exogenous amines, such as tyramine from certain foods and drinks, and drugs such as sympathomimetic amines, analgesics, antihistamines and anti-Parkinson drugs. The intake of exogenous amines when there is a concentration of MAO inhibitors in the body, can lead to further accumulation of endogenous amines resulting in severe headaches, hypertensive crises and even death.

ALTERATION OF ABSORPTION AND DISTRIBUTION

Many endogenous and exogenous substances are partially ionized at physiological pH values. Thus their absorption, general distribution, local concentrations and excretion can be affected by substances which alter the pH of a particular organ or biophase at a particular active site by either a direct or indirect effect.

The principles are illustrated by the following examples. Different diets can alter the pH of urine; subjects in West Africa on a balanced protein diet had pH values fluctuating about pH 6, while a corresponding group on a low protein diet had fluctuations about pH 7·5 (Fig. 9). The first group excreted 40 to 60 per cent of a dose of amphetamine unchanged in 16 hours,

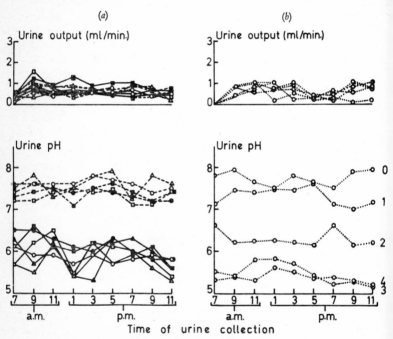

FIG. 9a. Urinary pH and flow rate in students and laboratory assistants on their normal diets.

Students: —□— A, —▲— B, —△— C, —●— D, —○— E, —■— J.
Laboratory assistants: ---●--- F, --□-- G, --○-- H, --△-- I.

FIG. 9b. Influence of change of diet on the urinary pH of laboratory assistant (F). o=urinary pH before change of diet. 1–4=urinary pH on first 4 days of increased protein diet. (similar patterns were obtained in other subjects).

whereas the second group excreted only about five per cent unchanged in the same period (Fig. 10). When additional protein was administered to the second group at breakfast, their urinary pH soon changed (Fig. 9, 11) to that of the first group and then like the first group they excreted unchanged amphetamine (Fig. 10) (Wesley-Hadzija, 1970). Earlier experiments had shown the relationship between urinary pH and the

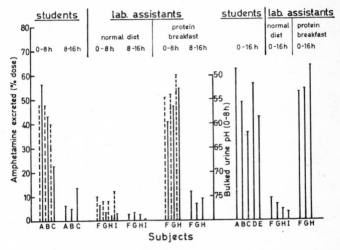

FIG. 10. Urinary excretion of amphetamine in students on balanced diet, and also laboratory assistants on normal carbohydrate diet and then on a carbohydrate plus protein diet for four days.

———: Excretion of amphetamine.
- - - - -: Urinary pH.

reabsorption of basic drugs, from kidney tubules (Beckett, Boyes and Tucker, 1968a, b; Beckett, 1969; Beckett, Salmon and Mitchard, 1969; Beckett et al., 1970). Retention of sympathomimetic drugs such as amphetamines in the body, which results in larger biological half-lives and more drug metabolism, produces greater behavioural effects than when these drugs are not reabsorbed from kidney tubules (Beckett et al., 1970). The alkaline pH conditions produced by some diets are likely to in-influence the reabsorption of endogenous amines possessing

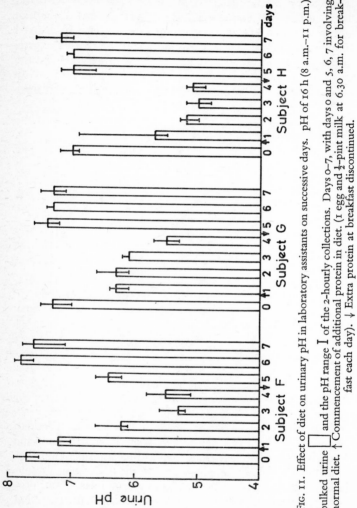

FIG. 11. Effect of diet on urinary pH in laboratory assistants on successive days. pH of 16 h (8 a.m.–11 p.m.) bulked urine ☐ and the pH range I of the 2-hourly collections. Days 0–7, with days 0 and 5, 6, 7 involving normal diet. ↑ Commencement of additional protein in diet. (1 egg and ½-pint milk at 6.30 a.m. for breakfast each day). ↓ Extra protein at breakfast discontinued.

differences in lipid solubility in their unionized and ionized forms.

Drinking alkaline liquids or using sodium bicarbonate makes the urine alkaline and results in longer biological half-lives for basic drugs and higher concentrations of their metabolites in the body. Similar effects are produced by those diuretics which produce alkaline urine.

Exercise, high protein diets and drinks of an acidic character make the urine acidic and reduce the amount of tubular reabsorption of basic drugs or basic exogenous materials but increase the tubular reabsorption of those acids which are lipid soluble in their unionized forms (Ariëns, 1969).

Changes in the distribution of foreign chemicals and endogenous hormones can result from competition between molecules for binding sites in plasma. Chemicals with acidic groups, such as salicylates, phenylbutazone, probenecid, sulphonamides, sulphinpyrazone, tolbutamide, methotrexate, coumarin anticoagulants, anti-inflammatory acidic drugs and steroids, and polycyclic compounds can compete for these binding sites (Anton, 1968; Christensen, Hansen and Kristensen, 1963; Brodie, 1965; Dixon, Henderson and Rall, 1965; Borga *et al.*, 1969) with consequent changes in circulating concentrations of 'free' material, and distribution and metabolism of these agents.

When active transport systems are involved in transferring material across biological membranes the possibility of mutual interference occurs. These carrier systems requiring energy are important in the transfer of acidic materials across membranes in the gut, kidney, liver and brain. Mutual interference has been shown for such materials as ethacrynic acid, amisometradine, probenecid, penicillin, phenylbutazone and salicylic acid (Brazeau, 1965; Ellenhorn and Sternad, 1966; Martin, 1964; Yü, Dayton and Gutman, 1963).

CHEMICAL/SUBSTRATE/ENZYME INTERACTIONS AT LOCAL
BIOPHASE LEVELS

The examples given above have dealt with the general aspects of mutual interactions that affect the general distribution, metabolism and excretion of chemicals. The above principles may be applied to a consideration of the local concentrations of drugs, chemicals, endogenous substrates, chemical transmitters, and enzymes in the CNS.

The role of adrenaline and noradrenaline in the adaptation to stress is well-known (Kety, 1966); abnormal states may be due to faulty adaptation to stimulation. It has been postulated that toxic mescaline-like compounds (Osmond and Smythies, 1952) or 3,4-dimethoxyphenylethylamine (Harley-Mason, 1952) are produced in faulty adaptation because of O-methylation of catecholamines rather than the normal N-methylation to produce adrenaline. Phenolase oxidation of adrenaline to adrenochrome in schizophrenics has been suggested (Hoffer, Osmond and Smythies, 1954). Because the N-methylation of nicotinamide to N-methylnicotinamide can compete with N-methylation of noradrenaline to adrenaline (methyl groups derived mainly from methionine), nicotinic acid has been administered to attempt to interfere with adrenaline and thus adrenochrome formation (Hoffer and Osmond, 1966).

N-dimethylation to produce N-dimethylated tryptamines may also play a role in brain malfunction since N,N-dimethyltryptamine (DMT) and N,N-dimethyl-5-hydroxytryptamine (bufotenine) evoke psychotic behaviour in humans (Böszörmenyi and Szàra, 1958); these compounds can be formed by N-dimethylation of the corresponding primary amines in animals (Axelrod, 1961). There may be reduced nicotinic acid production in some persons with a resultant increase in N-methylation of endogenous amines.

It has been postulated that it is the malfunctioning of the methylation process itself which is primarily responsible for the functional changes at both the neuronal and behavioural levels and that the production of the abnormal N-methylated compounds arises from this malfunction (Kety, 1961).

Biochemical methyl donors should play a role in the above effects; schizophrenic patients become worse when given the methyl donors, methionine and betaine, in the presence of monoamine oxidase inhibitors (Park, Baldessarini and Kety, 1965). It is therefore not surprising that methionine loading (Kety, 1966) and nicotinic acid administration (Hoffer, 1964) are being advocated for the treatment of schizophrenics.

Dopamine is a central neurotransmitter (McLennan and York, 1967) and particularly large amounts are found in basal ganglia

(Hornykiewicz, 1966). Patients exhibiting Parkinsonism have little dopamine in the basal ganglia; drugs causing the symptoms reduce the concentration of dopamine in the brain (Hornykiewicz, 1966; Calne *et al.*, 1969). Because the main action of dopamine on the basal ganglia is inhibiting and that of acetylcholine is excitatory, probably Parkinsonism is produced by an increase of the ratio of acetylcholine to dopamine at basal ganglia. Thus a reduction of acetylcholine or its action and an increase of dopamine at the site should remedy the complaint; this explains the use of anticholinergic drugs to deal with the former and L-dopa to deal with the latter. Dopa has to be given to produce dopamine in the brain by decarboxylation, since the latter does not pass the blood brain barrier. Inhibitors of dopadecarboxylase depress the peripheral decarboxylation of dopa and thus allow more of the amino acid to be available for penetration into the CNS; the combined administration of dopa and the enzyme inhibitors has thus made it possible to reduce the dose of dopa (Brücke, 1969; Tissot *et al.*, 1969).

The localization of the concentrations of the endogenous or exogenous chemicals in the CNS can seriously affect behaviour. Carbachol applied to the lateral hypothalamus via an implanted cannula, but not other neurohumoral drugs, changed non-killer rats into killers; acetylcholinesterase inhibitors had the same effect. The local concentration of acetylcholine thus seems to be implicated and the fact that the acetylcholine antagonist, methyl atropine, administered to the lateral hypothalamus changed killer into non-killer rats, supports this conclusion (Smith, King and Hoebel, 1970).

CONCLUSION

In the above account, examples have been given to indicate various ways in which circulating and local levels of chemical transmitters, and foreign substances which influence them in man, may be altered by the intake of drugs, food and foreign chemicals from man's environment. Many dramatic changes have resulted from the presence of these foreign substances in animals, but frequently the conditions, routes of administration and amounts used bear little relationship to conditions for man. In general, man is subjected to low doses of a wide variety of

potential enzyme inhibitors and stimulators; the various effects
may be mutually cancelling except when special foreign agents,
such as drugs, are used in larger doses to deal more selectively
with certain biochemical deficiencies or abnormalities. It is
important to keep our perspective in examining the non-critical
extrapolation of data to man from sometimes non-physiological,
atypical and irrelevant studies in animals. Comparative biochemical studies in different species under similar conditions are
imperative if we are to attempt to deal scientifically with the
potential problem of the effect of chemicals in our environment
on the behaviour of man.

It is to be hoped that over-reaction in decision making based
on inadequate information from experiments carried out under
non-physiological conditions in animals, as in the case of cycla-
mates, will not hinder progress in the development and use of
chemicals to enable man to produce and preserve more food,
to control pests, to enrich his life and to treat his illnesses and cure
his diseases.

REFERENCES

ANTON, A. H. (1968). *Clin. Pharmac. Ther.*, **9**, 561. [and references cited therein].
ARIËNS, E. J. (1969). *J. mond. Pharm.*, **12**, 263. [and references cited therein].
AXELROD, J. (1961). *Science*, **134**, 343.
BECKETT, A. H. (1969). *Pure appl. Chem.*, **19**, 231–248.
BECKETT, A. H., BOYES, R. N., and TUCKER, G. T. (1968*a*). *J. Pharm. Pharmac.*, **20**, 269–276.
BECKETT, A. H., BOYES, R. N., and TUCKER, G. T. (1968*b*). *J. Pharm. Pharmac.*, **20**, 277–282.
BECKETT, A. H., GORROD, J. W., and JENNER, P. G. (1970). *Biochem. Pharmac.*, in press.
BECKETT, A. H., SALMON, J. A., and MITCHARD, M. (1969). *J. Pharm. Pharmac.*, **21**, 251–258.
BORGA, O., AZARNOFF, D. L., FORSHELL, G. P., and SJÖQVIST, F. (1969). *Biochem. Pharmac.*, **18**, 2135.
BÖSZÖRMENYI, Z., and SZÀRA, S. (1958). *J. ment. Sci.*, **104**, 445.
BRAZEAU, P. (1965). In *The Pharmacological Basis of Therapeutics*, 3rd edn., p. 871, ed. Goodman, L. S., and Gilman, A. New York: Macmillan.
BRODIE, B. B. (1965). *Pro. R. Soc. Med.*, **58**, 946.
BRÜCKE, F. T. (1969). *Medsche Kurse ärztl. Fbldg*, **19**, 452.
CALNE, D. B., STERN, G. M., LAURENCE, D. R., SHARKEY, J., and ARMITAGE, P. (1969). *Lancet*, **1**, 744.
CHRISTENSEN, L. K., HANSEN, J. M., KRISTENSEN, M. (1963). *Lancet*, **2**, 1298.

CONNEY, A. H. (1969). *J. mond. Pharm.*, **12**, 186.

CRAWFORD, J. S., and RUDOFSKY, S. (1966). *Br. J. Anaesth.*, **38**, 446–454.

CUCINELL, S. A., CONNEY, A. H., SANSOR, M., and BURNS, J. J. (1965). *Clin. Pharmac. Ther.*, **6**, 420.

DIXON, R. L., HENDERSON, E. S., and RALL, D. P. (1965). *Fedn Proc. Fedn Am. Socs exp. Biol.*, **24**, 454.

ELLENHORN, M. J., and STERNAD, F. A. (1966). *J. Am. pharm. Ass.*, **6**, 62.

HARLEY-MASON, J. (1952). *J. ment. Sci.*, **98**, 309.

HOFFER, A. (1964). In *Nicotinic Acid and/or Nicotinamide for Treating Schizophrenia: A Compilation of Saskatchewan Research Information.* Regina: Whitecross.

HOFFER, A., and OSMOND, H. (1966). *How to live with Schizophrenia.* New York: University Books.

HOFFER, A., OSMOND, H., and SMYTHIES, J. (1954). *J. ment. Sci.*, **100**, 29.

HORNYKIEWICZ, O. (1966). *Pharmac. Rev.*, **18**, 925.

KATER, R. M. H., TOBON, F., and IBER, F. L. (1969). *J. Am. med. Ass.*, **207**, 363.

KETY, S. S. (1961). *Fedn Proc. Fedn Am. Socs exp. Biol.*, **20**, 849.

KETY, S. S. (1966). *Proceedings of the Second Symposium on Catecholamines,* Milan, 1965, pp. 787–798, ed. Acheson, G. H. Baltimore: Williams & Wilkins.

KOLMODIN, B., AZARNOFF, D. L., SJÖQVIST, F. (1969). *Clin. Pharmac. Ther.*, **10**, 638.

McLENNAN, H., and YORK, D. H. (1967). *J. Physiol., Lond.*, **189**, 393.

MARTIN, B. K. (1964). *Pharm. J.*, **193**, 119.

OSMOND, H., and SMYTHIES, J. (1952). *J. ment. Sci.*, **98**, 309.

PARK, L. C., BALDESSARINI, R. J., and KETY, S. S. (1965). *Archs gen. Psychiat.*, **12**, 346.

PRESCOTT, L. F. (1969). *Lancet*, **2**, 1239. [and references cited therein].

REMMER, H. (1969). *J. mond. Pharm.*, **12**, 169. [and references cited therein].

RUBIN, E., and LIEBER, C. S. (1968). *Science*, **162**, 690.

SMITH, D., KING, M., and HOEBEL, B. (1970). *Science*, **167**, 900.

TISSOT, R., GAILLARD, J.-M., GUGGISBERG, M., GAUTHIER, G., and AJURIAGUERRA, J. DE (1969). *Presse méd.*, **77**, 619–622.

TODD, R. G. (ed.) (1967). *Extra Pharmacopoeia: Martindale,* 25th edn, p. 1038. London: The Pharmaceutical Press. [and references cited therein].

WELCH, R. M., HARRISON, Y. E., GOMMI, B. W., POPPERS, P. J., FINSTER, M., and CONNEY, A. H. (1969). *Clin. Pharmac. Ther.*, **10**, 100.

WESLEY-HADZIJA, B. (1970). *J. Pharm. Pharmac.*, in press.

WHO (1969). *Tech. Rep. Ser. Wld Hlth Org.*, No. 427.

YÜ, T. F., DAYTON, P. G., and GUTMAN, A. B. (1963). *J. clin. Invest.*, **42**, 1330.

DISCUSSION

Kety: I am impressed with the data on the effects of urinary pH on the excretion of drugs. We should have realized the importance of this area. In the experiments in Ghana could you perceive differences in the clinical effects of amphetamine in the subjects, depending upon the urinary pH?

Beckett: Yes, in a subjective way. Quantitative assessments of the effects of amphetamine on humans is difficult. However when we altered the pH of urine artificially by administering sodium bicarbonate the effect was obvious; the subjects became much more aggressive than when the same dose of amphetamine was used when their urine was acid.

Sandler: As you have implied, this pH effect is also important for the excretion of endogenous substances. We have worked on the excretion of some biologically active monoamines and their metabolites (Sandler, Ruthven and Ceasar, 1967). Tryptamine excretion, for example, which has been widely used as an index of *in vivo* monoamine oxidase activity (Sjoerdsma, 1961), varies by a factor of about two depending on whether the urine is acid or alkaline; dopamine behaves similarly, but not noradrenaline, adrenaline, tyramine, or 5-hydroxytryptamine. Of the acid metabolites, it is well established that indoleacetic acid behaves similarly (Milne *et al.*, 1960) but in an opposite direction to tryptamine. The output of homovanillic acid and 4-hydroxy-3-methoxymandelic acid (VMA) does not vary with pH. The excretion of many of these compounds tends also to be volume dependent.

Beckett: We now have a "buccal test" to predict whether a drug will show pH dependence in excretion or be pH and volume dependent. When there is minimal tubular reabsorption of a chemical it is possible to examine differences in enzymatic activities in the subjects.

King: What effect does fasting have on urinary pH?

Beckett: Exercise makes the urine acid. Low protein diets tend to produce an alkaline urine.

Kety: The urine also becomes acid in starvation.

Beckett: It is interesting to link this information with clinical trials of drugs. In West Africa certain bases are likely to be more effective if one of their main routes of elimination is via the urine since the drug will be reabsorbed, whereas in East Africa, even on a low protein diet, the urine is acidic and thus basic drugs will be excreted.

Albert: Who are the people at risk in a population with respect to alkaline urine?

Beckett: One would need to know the percentage of people in the population with a urinary pH of above 7.

Spinks: The major groups with a high pH would be vegetarians and people with chronic peptic ulcers who take too much bicarbonate.

Beckett: Yes, but even without an obvious reason, certain people have an average pH of above 7.

Harris: What proportion of individuals in a population with a similar food intake have a high urinary pH.

Beckett: We looked at a few hundred people and only four or five had an average pH of above 7.

Harris: Have you looked at their families?

Beckett: No.

Kety: Assuming that one has eliminated people with respiratory difficulty, how can people on the same diet consistently show differences in pH? Where would the anions be coming from?

Boyland: Organic sulphur and phosphate are sources of acid. Cysteine is oxidized to sulphate and a strong acid is produced.

Joyce: In different conditions of urinary pH different amounts of ionized substances are reabsorbed. These might be metabolized by different routes; and the net total metabolism could remain the same. The whole story is not told by the amount of unchanged substance in the urine.

Beckett: Yes, but urinary pH can alter the rate of elimination of drug and metabolite relative to each other. Methylephedrine is highly susceptible to pH for its capacity to pass through a lipid membrane whereas phenylpropanolamine is not. Thus for methylephedrine or ephedrine, the ratio of metabolite to drug in the blood will be lower under acid than under alkaline conditions.

Kety: Would the influence of urinary pH be most marked in drugs for which the major mode of inactivation is via urinary excretion?

Beckett: Yes. By controlling urinary pH and thus tubular absorption of chemicals we are attempting to establish relative metabolic rates and routes for related compounds and thus investigating the effects of other drugs, chemicals and the environment on these rates and routes.

Harris: You showed the differences in alcohol metabolism

between heavy drinkers and social drinkers. Were you attributing the differences to enzyme induction?

Beckett: Possibly, but increased metabolic rates for alcohol may be present in subjects who drink heavily.

Harris: Can you demonstrate enzyme induction with barbiturates in animals?

Beckett: Yes.

Boyland: Enzyme induction is a problem with food additives. It is difficult to decide if compounds that induce enzymes present a hazard to man.

Harris: You gave a list of substances that cause induction. Are they specific inducers?

Beckett: In general this was non-specific induction.

Harris: Is there any evidence, with alcohol for example where we think that enzyme induction occurs, that this affects the metabolism of any other substances?

Beckett: This is at present being investigated.

Harris: I am interested in alcohol because there is good evidence (Von Wartburg, Papenberg and Aebi, 1965), from studies on liver biopsies and post-mortem material, for what appears to be a qualitative peculiarity in alcohol dehydrogenase in about 10 per cent of the cases.

REFERENCES

MILNE, M. D., CRAWFORD, M. A., GIRÃO, C. B., and LOUGHRIDGE, L. (1960). *Clin. Sci.*, **19,** 165.

SANDLER, M., RUTHVEN, C. R. J., and CEASAR, P. M. (1967). *Abstr. VII Int Congr. Biochem.*, Tokyo, p. 971.

SJOERDSMA, A. (1961). *J. Neuropsychiat.*, **2,** 159S.

WARTBURG, J. P. von, PAPENBERG, J., and AEBI, H. (1965). *Can. J. Biochem.*, **43,** 889–898.

ELECTROLYTES AND BEHAVIOUR IN MAN

P. H. VENABLES

Department of Psychology, Birkbeck College, University of London

THE nature of experimental work undertaken and the potential usefulness of the techniques used is largely a matter of faith that the observations which are made converge with the ideas and findings of other workers so as to provide a direction which seems worthwhile.

In work in any discipline there is a level of analysis that is appropriate to that discipline, but it is common for research workers to find that they are working on the boundaries of the expertise provided by the field in which they have been trained. This is so with the work that will be described and the suggestions derived from it.

It is probably useful at the onset to state the "articles of faith" upon which this paper is based. These are perhaps best stated as a quotation from Tschirgi (1960):

> "The functional capacity of every neuron within the nervous system is dependent upon the nature of the milieu which invests it. Minute changes in chemical or physical parameters of this microenvironment will alter the threshold of excitability in adjacent cell membranes and thereby influence functional activity . . . since the commodity of the nervous system is information, meaningless fluctuations in significant components of the neuronal environment will introduce noise in the communication sense, and it is not surprising, therefore, to discover unique homeostatic mechanisms designed to buffer the central nervous system against such changes and thereby to achieve a maximum signal to noise ratio."

It is beyond the bounds of the expertise of the psychologist (and, it would appear, also of the physiologist) to measure directly the electrolyte distribution of the environment of the nervous system. Indirect measures have to be employed, and some of the best known are those employing isotope dilution techniques. The findings of some studies (e.g. review by Coppen, 1967) suggest that changes in the distribution of sodium between intracellular and extracellular space accompany mental changes during episodes of depression and mania. The therapeutic use of lithium in bringing about beneficial alterations in the distribution of sodium provides a further demonstration of the influence of simple ionic exchanges upon neural function. The use of isotope dilution techniques is limited insofar as it is undesirable to use them again on the same patient or employ normal controls. However, it is possible to measure rates of excretion or retention of sodium in the parotid duct. By this means Glen, Ongley and Robinson (1969) showed a reduction in the transport of sodium into saliva in cases of depression and mania which parallels the finding of retention of sodium in these affective disorders shown by the isotope dilution method. This example is given to illustrate the concept that it may be useful to examine even a small part of the system which regulates the microenvironment of the nerve cells. In some cases it is convenient to measure the loss of retention of electrolytes in secreted fluids, and in others the electrical changes which appear to accompany active transport or which result from a particular ion distribution. It is always difficult to ascertain whether the measurements made are influenced by too many extraneous variables, or, indeed, whether "changes in electrolytes are causal or secondary to changes in mood"(Coppen, 1967).

It is similarly difficult to determine whether some of the changes in peripheral electrical activity which can be shown to be related to electrolyte status are epiphenomena or more direct indices of neural function. It has been shown that in groups of non-paranoid schizophrenics the degree of psycho-social withdrawal as a prime symptom of the illness is closely related to the tonic level of palmar skin potential (Venables and Wing, 1962). If, as appears to be the case, the skin potential measure bears some relation to electrolyte status, then it is possible that this is a further example of the influence of the distribution of body electrolytes on mental disturbances; on the other hand, the fact that we can conveniently record peripheral electrical activity may not be directly relevant. At this stage it seems worthwhile to pursue the possibility of potential usefulness and so follow the introduction of Professor Boyland that one of the purposes of the present meeting is to examine the value of tests which may indicate hazards to mental health.

The work I would like to describe is largely that of my colleagues Dr D. C. Fowles* and Mrs Margaret Christie.†

One of the major difficulties in studying man which is probably not fully accounted for is that of making measurements which do not as a result of the measurement process alter the state of the organism being measured. Much of the work on body fluids has made use of blood or urine. The withdrawal of blood, although a simple procedure, is stressful to the subject, while the production of urine samples has for the average person some socially embarrassing features which make it potentially mildly stressful. That even small changes in social conditions can produce marked endocrine changes which may through mineralocorticoid activity produce electrolyte changes is evident from the work of Mason and Brady (1965). For these reasons the use of other body fluids, or the use of electrical indices of electrolyte status is potentially useful. The body fluids we have used are sweat and saliva, and the electrical activity that of the skin and heart. As electrical activity has the additional advantage of being able to be telemetred, further removal from the disturbing influence of the laboratory is possible.

Two measures of electrical activity of the skin are possible; one measuring the conductivity of the skin to the passage of a very small current, the other, where no external current is passed, involves the measurement of potential differences developed between an "active" electrode placed on the palm, and an "indifferent" or "reference" electrode placed on an abraded site on the forearm. It is this latter measure of skin potential, because of its possible relation to electrolyte status, which will be mainly discussed. Lykken and his colleagues (1966) have suggested that the range over which electrical activity of the skin varies is an individual characteristic. The work to be described concentrates on the lower and upper limits of skin potential shown by an individual and attempts to determine mechanisms responsible for their production.

If a subject is allowed to rest in a quiet room after 10 to 20 minutes skin potential falls to a minimum value and thereafter

* Now of the University of Oklahoma.
† Birkbeck College, London.

rises slightly. This minimum value may be called basal skin potential level (BSPL). At this point, provided no sweat gland activity has taken place for some time, any contribution due to potential within the ducts may be considered to be minimal. The mean level of BSPL is in fact similar to that achieved after pharmacological elimination of sweat gland activity by ionto-phoresis of hyoscyamine (Venables and Martin, 1967). A high $(r = -0.70)$ correlation between the BSPL and the amplitude of the T-wave of the electrocardiogram suggested that BSPL might be some relatively simple membrane or liquid junction potential involving concentrations of potassium in the external electrolyte used to make electrode contact and some physiological level of potassium in the skin. The T-wave of the electrocardio-gram has been shown to reflect the concentration of potassium ions (K^+) in serum ... " When serum K^+ increases the first change is alteration of the T-wave which becomes high and peaked" (Darrow, 1950). Changes in body K^+ can be induced in normal subjects by oral administration of the ion (Mashima, Fu and Fukushima, 1965). Laks (1967) has stated that potassium transport across cell membranes is one of the major determinants of the amplitude of the T-wave, although Marriott (1960) lists a variety of physiological and pharmacological influences on the T-wave. Thus, if the amplitude of the T-wave bears a positive relation to extracellular potassium and a negative relation to palmar skin potential measured with potassium chloride as the external electrolyte, it is not unreasonable to suggest that skin potential is determined by some concentration difference between body and external electrolyte K^+, and can be described by an equation of the form $E = K \log \dfrac{C_{out}}{C_{in}}$ [where C_{out} is the concentration of external electrolyte and C_{in} is the concentration of internal (body) electrolyte]. The electrolyte concentration used externally was, in this instance, 0.5 g/100 ml KCL, or effectively 67 mequiv/K^+. When this concentration was systematically changed and the resultant potential measured, for any one person there was substantial agreement between the potential measured and that calculated with C_{out} at various values and C_{in} held constant. What is puzzling about these calculations is that the calculated value of C_{in} is about ten times that in plasma, suggesting a build-up in K^+ in the horny layer of the skin. That this build-up is a resultant of K^+ derived from plasma is suggested by the relation of K^+ to the amplitude of the T-wave. K^+ at the palmar surface was measured and a correlation of $r = -0.56$ was obtained between it and basal palmar skin potential.

A further indication that BSPL appeared to reflect electrolyte status was shown by the fact that the changes in its value due to diurnal variation parallel those in K^+ in transcellular fluids such as urine and saliva and are out of phase with change in psycho-physiological measures, such as skin conductance and heart rate, reflecting activity of the autonomic nervous system. At low levels of behavioural activity it appears possible to employ two direct measures of the concentration of K^+ outside the intracellular space; the T-wave of the electrocardiogram and the minimum level of palmar skin potential. At high levels of behavioural activation another set of factors is brought into play. It is well known that the resting membrane potential in nerve cells depends upon the active transport of sodium out of the cell against chemical and electrical potential gradients. Analogous active transport of ions occurs across epithelial membranes often more than one cell thick, and this is what appears to happen in the duct of the eccrine sweat glands in man, and also in the parotid and submaxillary salivary glands. There is general agreement that a "primary secretion", which is either isotonic or hypertonic in relation to plasma, is formed by the secretory cells in the coiled portion of the sweat gland. As the secretion passes down the duct, sodium is actively transported out of solution rendering it hypotonic on arrival at the surface. However, as the transport system is of limited capacity the concentration of the eventual sweat is related to the rate at which it is secreted. Chloride ions are not thought to be actively transported but to be reabsorbed passively as a result of the large electrical gradient generated by the sodium transport.

The most direct evidence for such a mechanism comes from the work of Schulz and his colleagues (1965) who found that the mean values for sodium and chloride concentration in sweat from the secretory coil were 147 and 123 mequiv/l, respectively, while the average values from sweat appearing at the surface of the skin were 22 mequiv/l for sodium, and 2 mequiv/l for chloride. The potential difference between sweat in the duct and interstitial fluid has a mean value of 50 mV (negative at the electrode in the sweat). Since similar processes appear to take place in the secretion of sweat and saliva, a negative relation between the concentration of sodium ions in the saliva and palmar skin potential would be predicted. Correlations of $r = -0.46$ and $r = 0.61$ were found in two experiments which examined this prediction (Fowles and Venables, 1968). Sodium reabsorption in sweat and salivary ducts is largely under the control of aldosterone, the secretion of which can be stimulated by ACTH (Fortier, 1962), and can consequently be thought of as resulting from physical and psychological stress. Effective stimuli for the stimulation of aldosterone have included medical school examinations, military combat and the presentation of scientific papers (Oken, 1967). Aldosterone secretion has been shown to be related to the state of anxiety exhibited by patients (Elmadjian, 1962), and a related preliminary finding by Fowles and myself has shown a relation between the Neuroticism scale of the Maudsley Personality Inventory and the extent of sodium reabsorption in saliva. More work, however, needs to be done before this latter finding can be considered secure.

Aldosterone is probably involved in potassium excretion as well as in sodium retention (McLean, 1961) and can be stimulated indirectly via the sympathetic-catecholamine system. Catecholamines induce a loss of K^+ from liver cells during the glycogenolysis which accompanies the reaction of "preparation for fight or flight" (Cannon, 1932). Such a loss of intracellular K^+ results in a transient increase in extracellular K^+ which acts as a stimulus for aldosterone.

To examine the secretion of cations in sweat and saliva and the electrical activity which accompanies, or is a byproduct of, this process is to study only a small corner of the process by which homeostasis is maintained in the *milieu intérieur*. The role of the kidneys would appear to be more extensive. However, the convenience involved in the measure of electrical activity by collection of sweat on a simple pad fastened to the skin, or of saliva by a dental roll, suggests that this line of work is worth pursuing.

Concern was expressed at the outset that investigations of this kind were on the borderline of several disciplines and it was suggested that a stand had to be taken about how far the levels of analysis should be extended. Measurement of electrophysiological activity carried out with full awareness of at least the major problems does not *necessarily* involve a deeper study of all the underlying factors. In a similar way the relatively simple measurement of cation excretion, either by flame photometer techniques or the use of ion selective glass electrodes, does not necessarily involve a fine grain analysis of the factors involved in the process.

What is clearly required are more studies which relate behaviour to these indices of electrolyte status. The amount of work using the measurement of skin potential levels in relation to behaviour has been small in comparison to that using skin conductance. Apart from the studies relating schizophrenic sub-diagnosis to skin potential level which have already been mentioned (e.g. Venables and Wing, 1962), a study by Spain (1966) relating conditionability and withdrawal in schizophrenics to skin potential level, and work by Shapiro and Leiderman (1965) on social factors and skin potential, no work relating skin potential level and behaviour has been reported. There have been even fewer studies where salivary or sweat cations have been related to behaviour, an exception being the work of Grad, Kral, and Cramer-Azima (1964) which showed that the sodium concentration in saliva correlated negatively and significantly with a memory test of complex recent verbal recall.

More direct work on the effects of electrolytes on behaviour is summarized by John (1967). In these studies injections of electrolytes into the central nervous system brought about changes in cortical excitability. However, even when this was so, changes in performance did not necessarily take place. John suggests that electrolyte shifts are involved in the coupling of the early labile phase of memory to the ensuing stable storage of information.

There are clearly insufficient data for any firm statement to be made in the field. However, it is possible to forsee a worthwhile future for studies in this area on the grounds that understanding the means whereby, and the effectiveness with which, individuals protect the microenvironment of their nervous systems in response to external assaults is of crucial importance. And also the extent to which the microenvironment is changed in response to external factors, or the extent to which there are individual differences in electrolyte balance, can provide insights into the relationship between electrolyte distribution and behaviour.

5

SUMMARY

The level of electrolytes providing the environment of neural and muscular cells is under tight regulatory control. Nevertheless, changes in mineralocorticoid activity due to external stresses do bring about changes in electrolyte states which may in turn result in changes in behaviour. Socially acceptable means of indirectly monitoring extracellular electrolytes offer the possibility of examining changes in these in man in a relatively free "non-laboratory" setting. Sweat and saliva are fluids which may be collected in a socially more acceptable fashion than blood or urine and under suitable conditions give rise to electrical changes at the skin surface which are easily monitored and capable of being telemetered.

REFERENCES

CANNON, W. B. (1932). *The Wisdom of the Body.* New York: Norton.

COPPEN, A. (1967). *Br. J. Psychiat.*, **113,** 1237–1264.

DARROW, D. C. (1950). *New Engl. J. Med.*, **242,** 1014–1018.

ELMADJIAN, F. (1962). In *Ultrastructure and Metabolism of the Nervous System,* pp. 414–419, ed. Korey, S. R., Pope, A., and Robins, E. Baltimore: Williams & Wilkins.

FORTIER, C. (1962). *A. Rev. Physiol.*, **24,** 223–258.

FOWLES, D. C., and VENABLES, P. H. (1968). *Psychonomic Sci.*, **10,** 387–388.

GLEN, A. I. M., ONGLEY, G. C., and ROBINSON, K. (1969). *Nature, Lond.,* **221,** 565–566.

GRAD, B., KRAL, V. A., and CRAMER-AZIMA, F. (1964). In *Recent Advances in Biological Psychiatry,* vol. 7, pp. 97–106, ed. Wortis, J. New York: Plenum.

JOHN, E. R. (1967). *Mechanisms of Memory.* New York: Academic Press.

LAKS, M. M. (1967). *Dis. Chest,* **51,** 573–586.

LYKKEN, D. T., ROSE, R., LUTHER, B., and MALEY, M. (1966). *Psychol. Bull.,* **66,** 481–484.

McLEAN, F. C. (1961). In *Mineral Metabolism: An Advanced Treatise,* pp. 1–10, ed. Comar, C. L., and Bronner, F. L. New York: Academic Press.

MARRIOTT, H. J. L. (1960). *Ann. intern. Med.,* **54,** 413–427.

MASHIMA, S., FU, L., and FUKUSHIMA, K. (1965). *Jap. Heart J.,* **6,** 463–473.

MASON, J. W., and BRADY, J. V. (1965). In *Psychobiological Approaches to Social Behaviour,* pp. 4–23, ed. Leiderman, P. H., and Shapiro, D. London: Tavistock.

OKEN, D. (1967). In *Psychological Stress: Issues in Research,* pp. 43–61, ed. Appley, M. H., and Trumball, R. New York: Appleton-Century-Crofts.

SCHULZ, I., ULLRICH, K. J., FRÖMTER, E., HOLZGREVE, H., FRICK, A., and HEGEL, U. (1965). *Pflügers Archiv. ges. Physiol.*, **284**, 360–372.

SHAPIRO, D., and LEIDERMAN, P. H. (1965). In *Psychobiological Approaches to Social Behaviour*, pp. 110–126, ed. Leiderman, P. H., and Shapiro, D. London: Tavistock.

SPAIN, B. (1966). *J. abnorm. Psychol.*, **71**, 260–266.

TSCHIRGI, R. D. (1960). In *Handbook of Physiology*, pt. 1, Neurophysiology, vol. 3, pp. 1865–1890, ed. Magoun, H. W. Bethesda: American Physiological Society.

VENABLES, P. H., and MARTIN, I. (1967). *Psychophysiology*, **3**, 302–311.

VENABLES, P. H., and WING, J. K. (1962). *Arch. gen. Psychiat.*, **7**, 114–119.

DISCUSSION

Boyland: Would you expect diuretics or an increased salt intake to affect behavioural performance?

Venables: One can look on this in the same way as one looks on any other effect of stress. As long as the system can cope there may be no effect on behaviour, but when the regulatory system is no longer effective the effects become toxic.

Spinks: Instead of looking for a small electrolyte change in mental disorder, wouldn't it be more rational to look for a large mental change in patients in whom a large electrolyte disorder is present?

Venables: Certainly, but I wonder whether in looking at the effects of the chemical environment we know what to look for. I suggest that rather than look at behaviour we might look at the way man protects his internal environment, which is what regulates behaviour.

Brimblecombe: How steady is your baseline within and between individuals. In particular, is it possible to find any difference in the electrolyte content of emotional versus thermal sweat?

Venables: Yes, it is. There is not much thermal sweating on the palm until one reaches 70°F; thus, if one works below this temperature, one can determine the electrolyte content of purely emotional sweat.

Brimblecombe: What are the diurnal rhythms for the electrolytes?

Venables: Not much is known about this. The diurnal rhythm of arousal, measured by heart rate or skin conductance, is completely out of phase with the diurnal rhythm of electrolyte shifts. We are evidently measuring something different in these two areas.

So it is important to take account of diurnal variations and do one's experiments at the same time of day.

Albert: Are any electrolyte changes associated with depression in normal people? Can you tell how you are feeling by measuring the electrolyte concentrations in your saliva?

Venables: Yes. What started me on this work was Bovard's (1959) comments on the effects of social stress. He wrote that in disturbing situations the taste of saliva changes and that this is due to a change in the sodium:potassium ratio in saliva.

Harris: I would like to generalize about how this sort of approach might be used in investigating schizophrenia. I imagine the frequency of schizophrenia in the population is of the order of one in 200. Is that correct?

Kety: Yes, or it may be more than this, depending on what definition of schizophrenia is used.

Harris: From the genetic data on schizophrenia we would conclude that only about one in five of the genetically predisposed in the population actually develops the disease. So we should be looking for the one in forty normal people who show an aberrant response to any test, physiological, psychological or behavioural, or to drugs. One can then study the familial distribution of this particular response. Thus one might discover which particular elements in the environment bring out aberrant responses. There is always a great danger in studies on so-called normality just to take a mean of the distribution and ignore the exceptional cases.

Venables: I agree. I talked about a general approach, but in fact all the time we are looking particularly at individual differences.

Cowley: There are marked differences in the amount of perspiration produced by different ethnic groups. In Uganda, Africans have lower concentrations of sodium in their sweat than Indians do. The Africans also have a lower sodium intake (McCance and Purohit, 1969). I did some work on children with a history of kwashiorkor (unpublished findings) and found that children that had "recovered" clinically showed greater latencies in their psychogalvanic response. Would you comment on the slowness of response in these circumstances?

Venables: It is difficult to think of anything in the sweat/electrolyte field that would bring about a change in the latency of the response. Mednick's (1967) work in Copenhagen on the children of schizophrenic mothers is relevant, however, The feature which most distinguished the children who later developed schizophrenia was the recovery phase after the skin resistance response: that is, the time taken for the level of resistance to return to the baseline from the peak value of the response (Fig. 1.) For example, with a pre-stimulation resistance of 50 kilohms across the palm, a stimulus might result in a fall of 5 kilohms.

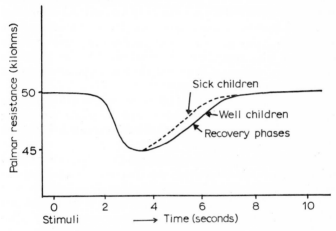

FIG. 1 (*Venables*). The skin resistance response (see, text).

The rate of return to the pre-stimulus level is the aspect of the wave form that distinguishes the children who later became sick from those who at the age of 20 years are still well.

Albert: Is this due to sweating?

Venables: This is a sweat response. The work of Edelberg (1970) suggests that the recovery leg of the response is due to reabsorption of water into the surrounding tissue. Sodium reabsorption might also be implicated.

Spinks: How can you exclude a purely nervous origin of this prolonged sweat response? It might be due to more prolonged reverberation of the nervous circuits from which the stimulus arises?

Albert: That is just the point. The sweat-response may be

useful in defining underlying physiological mechanisms that play a part in the behavioural response.

Venables: There can be different prolongations of the sweat response resulting from the same duration of stimulation of the direct nervous pathways responsible for sweat-gland activity.

Kety: To what extent is galvanic skin resistance (GSR) a measure of electrolyte concentration in the sweat, and to what extent is it simply a measure of the amount of sweating?

Venables: One has to separate skin conductance due to the passage of an external current—the GSR—from the skin potential measured without an external current. I was originally talking about skin potential, which does seem to be a phenomenon connected with electrolyte concentrations. As far as the skin conductance response is concerned, the GSR response may occur in the absence of overt sweat secretion.

Boyland: Food intake must effect the microenvironment so one would expect vegetarians to have a higher potassium: sodium ratio than meat eaters. Could this explain differences in behaviour?

Venables: We tried to investigate this by giving one group of subjects a potassium-restricted diet and another group a diet high in potassium, but we were unsuccessful in our attempts.

Albert: Both thermal and emotional sweat is discharged in a pulsatile fashion with peaks about every eight seconds. This probably reflects the periodic activity of the autonomic nervous system. Is there any evidence that there are differences in this discharge with respect to emotional or mental illness?

Venables: One is measuring the integrated effect of many sweat glands. It is just possible at low levels of sweating to see suggestions of a pulsatile discharge in the GSR but this would be difficult to measure.

Albert: This type of phenomenon may be related to rhythmic variations in vasomotor tone. Could the differences in response that were obtained from future schizophrenics and from normal subjects be related to differences in the periodic activity of the sympathetic nervous system?

Spinks: Does enhanced urinary catecholamine concentration occur in pre-schizophrenic children? Has anyone studied this?

Kety: Pollin and Stabenau (1968) have examined monozygotic twins discordant for schizophrenia in an effort to separate environmental from genetic factors. Pollin (unpublished) found recently that corticosteroid excretion was higher in the schizophrenic than in the normal twin but catecholamine excretion was raised in both twins. This work suggests that a high level of catecholamine synthesis may be a predisposing factor for schizophrenia.

REFERENCES

BOVARD, E. W. (1959). *Psychol. Rev.*, **66**, 267–276.

EDELBERG, R. (1970). *Psychophysiology*, in press.

McCANCE, R. A., and PUROHIT, G. (1969). *Nature, Lond.*, **221**, 378–379.

MEDNICK, S. A. (1967). *The Origins of Schizophrenia*, pp. 179–200, ed. Romano, J. Excerpta Medica: Amsterdam.

POLLIN, W., and STABENAU, J. R. S. (1968). In *The Transmission of Schizophrenia*, pp. 317–332, ed. Rosenthal, D., and Kety, S. S. Oxford: Pergamon.

SOME EFFECTS OF ALCOHOL UPON HUMAN COOPERATION: AN EXPERIMENTAL QUANTITATIVE APPROACH

C. R. B. JOYCE,* LYNN PAN† AND D. D. VARONOS‡

Department of Pharmacology and Therapeutics, London Hospital Medical College, London

IT is now well known that the physiological responses of an individual to a drug may be modified by interactions with other people (see Joyce, 1965). The part played by drugs in modifying interactions between individuals has received less attention, despite its rather obvious social and political importance. Some knowledge of the extent to which economic and other decisions are made in the presence of alcohol lies within the experience of most adults (Davis, 1968); and information about the medical treatment received by national leaders is becoming more widely disseminated in the popular press (Fairley, 1966; Moran, 1966). The development of laboratory methods of examining the effects of drugs upon social interactions is essential. A technique recently developed by Hammond (1965) not only represents an interesting simulation of real-life decision-making, but also yields a large number of response measures which are readily quantifiable. It has already been applied to the study of national differences in decision-making (Hammond *et al.*, 1968). Our use of the method in social psychopharmacology was first briefly reported elsewhere (Joyce *et al.*, 1968).

Different personalities react differently to drugs; the effects of alcohol are no exception. Variations in "extraversion-introversion" (E-I) (Eysenck, 1963) are known to be relevant. Alcohol lowers central inhibition and so makes one person more socially available to another, but it does so with varying effectiveness depending on the end of the E-I Scale at which the subject falls. A prevailing tendency to enhanced excitation in the extravert may be related to his more marked response to "depressants",

* Present address: Medical Department, CIBA AG, CH 4000 Basel 7, Switzerland
† Present address: P.O. Box 242, Kota Kinabalu, Sabah, Malaysia
‡ Present address: Department of Pharmacology, University of Athens Medical School, Athens, Greece

and may be manifested as behaviour in which trained reactions give way to substantially modified responses, especially if made in the absence of feedback or reward. In contrast, the behaviour of the introvert is less changed by alcohol, and the effect of his previous training is more persistent. The E-I dimension may well be relevant to the effect of alcohol upon decision-making, which is likely to be influenced by many other factors which have not been so intensively studied, if at all, in relation to alcohol. A habitual disposition to enter a social situation in certain ways which will make for ease or difficulty in reaching agreement on controversial issues may be created by the subject's cognitive style—for example, his tendency to use "divergent" or "convergent" thinking (Getzels and Jackson, 1962; Hudson, 1962), by his proneness to authoritarianism (Adorno et al., 1950), or by emotional factors often referred to as neurotic and reputedly assessed by appropriate inventories (Eysenck, 1963). Some combinations of differences in such characteristics, not only in the individual but in the pair, might favour compromise more than others. For example, a tendency on the part of an introverted individual to hold authoritarian views and to think in a socially stereotyped rather than an innovatory way might be manifested as a considerable resistance to change from a previously maintained position in the experimental task. On the other hand, the interaction of two extraverted but divergent individuals might also prolong attempts to reach agreement. Information about these aspects of the personalities of interacting subjects was therefore collected during experiments on the effect of alcohol on Hammond's experimental task.

METHODS

The experiment was carried out in two parts. The second series replicated the first in all respects except in the manner of selecting and training the subjects.

The task

The experimental situation has been briefly described by Hammond (1965) but the salient points are as follows (Table I). Members of two-person groups attempt to reach agreement on a cognitive task to which they are likely to make different initial

TABLE I

EXPERIMENTAL PROCEDURE

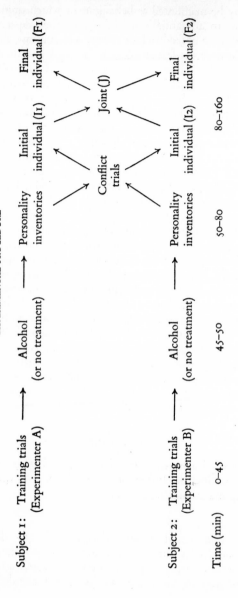

Subject 1:	Training trials (Experimenter A)	→	Alcohol (or no treatment)	→	Personality inventories	
						Initial individual (I_1) → Final individual (F_1)
						Conflict trials → Joint (J)
Subject 2:	Training trials (Experimenter B)	→	Alcohol (or no treatment)	→	Personality inventories	Initial individual (I_2) → Final individual (F_2)
Time (min)	0–45		45–50		50–80	80–160

responses as a result of previous experimental training. Unknown to the other, each member of the pair is previously trained to respond in a different way to the material presented, which in the present case was concerned with judgments about the political development of a number of (hypothetical) countries. After the initial period of individual training, the subjects are brought together. They first privately record their personal judgments about each new test case, then announce them and discuss them publicly until agreement has been reached, when they make their final decisions privately once again.

Subjects

Two groups, each of 12 pairs of volunteer medical students aged between 19 and 22 years, took part in the experiments. One female pair and two mixed pairs took part in the second experiment; all the other pairs were male. The first study began with a sample of 18 pairs, 12 of which were selected, after completing a preliminary run on the task, to represent three subgroups of equal size. Groups of high and low conflict pairs were designated on the basis of the total ranked differences between the initial private scores of their members as well as the ranked number of initial difference scores above (or below) the median for the whole group. The remaining four pairs were designated of medium conflict.

The 12 pairs of subjects in the second experiment did not undergo preliminary selection, but were classified at the end of the study in the same way as in the first experiment, by means of the extent of initial differences shown in the control (no alcohol) run. Of these, three pairs fell into the high conflict category, three in the low, and the remaining six pairs were in the intermediate category.

Experimental design and procedure (Table II)

In each experiment the subjects were tested twice; half the pairs received the equivalent of 60 ml of absolute ethyl alcohol in the form of 65 per cent proof vodka on the first occasion. The other half received the same treatment on the second occasion. During the control sessions no alcohol or substitute drink was given, since the study was concerned with the alcohol *situation*, and not with the pharmacological effect of alcohol as such,

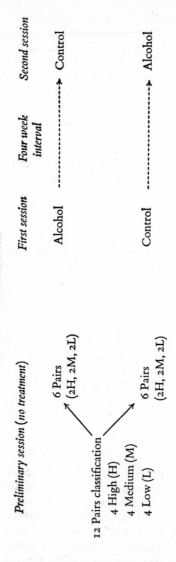

TABLE II

DESIGN OF EXPERIMENT ONE

Preliminary session (no treatment)

12 Pairs classification
4 High (H)
4 Medium (M)
4 Low (L)

6 Pairs (2H, 2M, 2L)

6 Pairs (2H, 2M, 2L)

First session

Alcohol

Control

Four week interval

Second session

Control

Alcohol

For the same reason the dose was not adjusted for body weight. The testing sessions all took place at the same time of day and the interval between sessions for a given pair was approximately four weeks. At each session half an hour elapsed between the time of receiving the drink and beginning the task. During this period subjects were asked to complete three personality questionnaires, namely: the Maudsley Personality Inventory, the California F Scale (Forms 40 and 45), and a test of Convergent/Divergent thinking (Joyce and Hudson, 1968).

The subjects were seated at opposite ends of a table and each was prevented by a screen from seeing the response sheets of the other. Each member of the pairs was trained in a separate room, either by L.P. or D. V., and the "conflict" sessions were all run by the same experimenter (L.P.) in the presence of her colleague (D.V.)

Measures of experimental conflict

Hammond's technique yields a number of measures, based upon differences between various judgments: for example, between

(1) the initial decisions that each member of the pair made as an individual: I_1-I_2.
(2) their final private judgments: F_1-F_2.
(3) their initial and joint judgments: I_1-J, I_2-J.
(4) their initial and final judgments: $(I_1$ or $I_2)-(F_1$ or $F_2)$.
(5) their final and joint judgments: F_1-J, F_2-J.
(6) the extent to which any of these departed from what would have been predicted from their training: T_1-I_1, T_2-I_2, T_1-F_1, T_1-J etc.
(7) the extent to which each approximated the "correct" answer (i.e., the value which the training stimuli would have elicited as the response in the absence of the deliberately introduced random variation (Hammond, 1965): I_1-C_1, F_2-C_2 etc.

In addition, the mean values of the initial, final and "correct" judgments can be calculated for each pair and are designated I, F and C. Values of all these variables, for each pair and trial as well as the means for each experiment, were calculated from the raw scores on the University of Colorado Computer Center IBM 7097 computer, using the programme kindly made available by Dr K. R. Hammond. Analyses of variation due to differences in treatment, order of treatment, and conflict were made with a desk calculator in our own laboratory.

RESULTS

In general, but not always, measures of conflict were lower on the second occasion (Table III and Fig. 1), expressed as a percentage

TABLE III

GROUP DATA FOR ORDER EFFECT ON TWO CONFLICT MEASURES ON TWO OCCASIONS

Measure	Experiment	Group	Mean score %		Order effect	
			1st	2nd	F-Ratio	Probability
Training–Initial	1	CA	42	35	7·9	<0·05
		AC	37	34		
	2	CA	56	51	6·1	<0·05
		AC	52	41		
Initial–Final	1	CA	47	36	10·1	<0·01
		AC	44	32		
	2	CA	37	47	14·0	<0·01
		AC	44	51		

CA: Control 1st session—Alcohol 2nd session
AC: Alcohol 2nd session—Control 1st session

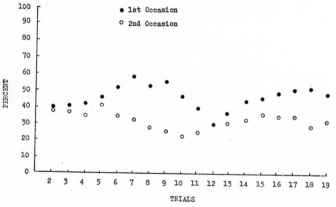

FIG. 1. Mean changes in I–F within trials, by order, in experiment 1.

of the maximal conflict score theoretically possible. However, conflict was more likely to increase on the second occasion in the second experiment (Fig 2).

Of 72 *F*-ratios obtained by the analyses of variance, 11 were likely to have occurred by chance on fewer than 1 in 20 occasions—5 in fact were so large as to have been likely on fewer than 1 in 100 replications of the experiment under the same conditions (Table IV). A statistically significant difference associated with differences in treatment (alcohol versus no alcohol) was detected

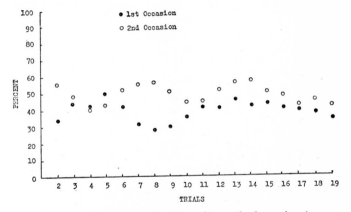

FIG. 2. Mean changes in I–F within trails, by order, in experiment 2.

for J–F in the first experiment and for F1–F2 in the second experiment: the interaction between treatments and conflict levels was significantly different from that due to chance, but it was of course at the end of this experiment that the pairs were categorized in respect of their initial degree of conflict in the alcohol-free session.

Seven of the eleven significant differences, however, were observed to occur in relation to variation attributable to "order"—that is, differences in performance on the first and second sessions, regardless of conflict level, treatment or other factors. Two of the three such observations made in the first experiment (T–I, at $P < 0.05$, and I–F at $P < 0.01$) were in fact repeated among the four significant differences in the second experiment, at the same level of likelihood in each case (Table III) but in the case of I–F

TABLE IV

F-RATIOS FOR BETWEEN AND WITHIN PAIRS VARIANCE IN MEASURES OF CONFLICT

	I_1-I_2	F_1-F_2	T-I	T-F	J-I	I-F	J-F	C-I	C-F
EXPERIMENT 1									
BETWEEN PAIRS									
Conflict	0·2	0·9	1·0	0·7	1·1	2·4	1·0	0·3	1·0
Treatment and conflict	0·0	0·1	1·0	0·0	0·4	0·2	0·3	0·0	0·0
WITHIN PAIRS									
Treatment	0·2	0·1	1·3	0·0	1·2	0·1	3·9★	0·1	0·1
Order	0·0	1·7	7·9★	4·4★	0·1	10·1†	0·0	0·1	0·1
EXPERIMENT 2									
BETWEEN PAIRS									
Conflict	5·9★	16·6†	0·3	0·1	2·4	0·3	3·5	1·8	0·5
Treatment and conflict	1·1	4·8†	0·1	0·0	0·1	0·5	0·0	0·2	0·1
WITHIN PAIRS									
Treatment	0·1	0·3	1·8	2·6	1·2	0·1	0·6	2·0	0·0
Order	1·4	0·3	6·1★	0·7	3·1	14·0†	0·0	4·6★	3·5†

★ $P < 0.05$
† $P < 0.01$

TABLE V

MEAN SCORES (±S.D.) ON MEASURES OF EXTRAVERSION/INTROVERSION (E/I) NEUROTICISM (N), AUTHORITARIANISM (F) AND CONVERGENCE/DIVERGENCE (C/D)

(n = 24 for each score)

	E/I	N	F	C/D
Experiment 1	26·5±11·0	26·0±9·5	96·3±14·6	10·1±3·2
Experiment 2	25·2±9·00	24·8±10·5	105·1±5·0	11·6±1·9
t	0·45	0·43	2·79	2·59
P	>0·6	>0·6	<0·02>0·01	<0·02>0·01

Test-retest reliability (session 1–session 2)

	E/I	N	F	C/D
Experiment 1	0·95	0·87	0·85	0·83
Experiment 2	0·85	0·91	0·86	0·65

in the opposite direction. The relationships are consistently present over all trials in the sessions (apart from a reversal of short duration at the start of experiment 2) as is clear from the three-point running average scores plotted in Figs. 1 and 2.

The individuals participating in the two experiments differed significantly in respect of the four personality inventories administered at each session of the two experiments (Table V). The 24 subjects of experiment 2 were on average both more "authoritarian" and more "divergent" ($0 \cdot 01 < P < 0 \cdot 02$ for both measures); the correlation between the two measures was significant though negative (see below). It is also to be noted that the test-retest reliability exceed $0 \cdot 83$ for seven of the eight measures obtained (i.e., between 69 and 90 per cent of the observed variation was contributed by consistent differences between individuals), but for the measure of convergence/divergence in experiment 2 the test-retest reliability was only $0 \cdot 65$ (i.e., only 42 per cent of the variation was attributable to stable individual differences).

Neuroticism correlated significantly with divergence in experiment 1 ($r = +0 \cdot 48$, $P < 0 \cdot 05$) as well as in experiment 2 ($r = +0 \cdot 54$) and (negatively) with authoritarianism in experiment 2 ($r = -0 \cdot 48$, $P < 0 \cdot 05$). These relationships are consistent with previous work (Hudson, 1962).

The relationships between the measures of conflict and the personality variables were also explored (Table VI). Four such coefficients, considered alone, were unlikely to have occurred by chance; but such a constellation in a total of 48 measures could well occur by chance (Sakoda, Cohen and Beall, 1954). As no consistent pattern was discernible between the two experiments and any significant relationship disappeared when the two sets of observations were combined, the two sets of variables were apparently no more than randomly associated.

The mean time taken to achieve agreement was $1 \cdot 6$ minutes per card presented (range 25 seconds to $15 \cdot 0$ minutes) and $32 \cdot 6$ minutes per whole test of 20 cards (range $16 \cdot 7$ to $81 \cdot 7$ minutes: Table VII). Over 80 per cent of the variance was contributed by consistent differences between pairs, and differences due to treatments or occasions did not reach conventional levels of significance. However, the interaction between treatments and occasions was significant. Alcohol apparently inter-

TABLE VI

CORRELATIONS OF MEASURES OF CONFLICT AND PERSONALITY

Experiment 1	Extra-version	Neuroti-cism	Authori-tarianism	Convergence/Divergence
T–I	0·09	0·13	0·24	0·29
T–J	0·04	0·05	0·24	0·18
T–F	0·12	0·02	0·48★	0·18
I–J	0·00	0·09	0·22	0·41★
I–F	0·14	0·20	0·24	−0·04
F–J	0·01	−0·04	−0·28	0·40★
Experiment 2				
T–I	0·30	0·22	0·08	0·01
T–J	0·21	0·13	0·03	0·03
T–F	0·37	0·20	−0·01	0·03
I–J	0·18	0·21	0·05	−0·25
I–F	0·29	0·44★	−0·08	−0·17
F–J	0·01	0·27	0·14	−0·03

★0·02> P >0·05

TABLE VII

TOTAL TEST TIME: EXPERIMENT I $(\text{SECONDS} \times 10^{-2})$

Pair	1	2	4	6	7	8	9	10	12	14	15	16	Totals
Alcohol first	23			27		19	16			19	14		118
Alcohol second		25	11		45			11	16			15	123
													241
Control first		30	15		49			25	16			16	151
Control second	13			18		10	14			12	10		77
													228
Total	36	55	26	45	94	29	30	36	21	31	24	31	469

fered with the practice effect between the first and second occasions—the mean reduction in total test time was 11·4 minutes if alcohol was taken first, 7·8 minutes if it was taken second.

DISCUSSION

The significant differences in conflict scores between the first and second occasions were not all in the same direction in the two experiments, and it seems, therefore, that training as such does not necessarily reduce conflict in this situation. Marked differences were found in both experiments between the occasions on which subjects had had alcohol and those when they had not but these were associated with the order of the session in the sequence, rather than with whether alcohol had been taken. The effect of drugs, even alcohol, upon measures of personality has been little studied. Only the measure of convergence/divergence was at all unstable. It may therefore be relatively more sensitive to alcohol, or (since it was administered when little alcohol would have been absorbed) to other concurrent influences.

The significant relationships between four measures of personality and the conflict scores were of modest size, and disappeared when the data from both experiments were combined.

Various explanations for the absence of demonstrable interaction between the measures of conflict and personality are possible. The limited range of responses permitted by the structure of the experimental situation may not have allowed differences in personality sufficient play to affect conflict behaviour. The high level of the intellectual capacity of the subjects may also have lessened possible effects of the underlying interpersonal variables. However, they were clearly well-motivated by the task and in many instances spent a very long time arguing about a particular trial.

More important attributes of personality than those studied may also have been overlooked. The Minnesota Multi-phasic Personality Index (MMPI) Dominance Scale, for instance, might have been more meaningful. It appears more likely, however, that attention should be paid to dynamic aspects of the impressions made by one member of a pair on his partner. For example, although the behaviour of a subject with a high extraversion score might be expected to change more under the influence of alcohol than that of his more introverted partner, if the latter were aware of the increased verbalization and greater social ease of his partner he might compromise more readily, so that the final judgments of the more extraverted member of the pair might deviate less from his original responses than would have been expected. Other predictions could be made in terms of different personality measures, to form the basis of stringent tests.

A very recent study (Bonaiuto and Bartoli, 1970) has in fact shown that benzoctamine, given for 21 days before the trial, not only reduces aggressiveness in neurotic subjects but also reduces the conflict scores when such subjects are paired together in the situation described here.

Though no clear answers were forthcoming to the original questions about the effect of alcohol upon the process of reaching agreement, the method used certainly yields a number of quantitative measures, and these have been shown to be sensitive to variations in experimental procedure. Hammond and his colleagues have recently shown that the method can be employed on a variety of topics other than the rather artificial political situations used here and in most of the other studies from his group, and that it can also be used on untrained subjects who manifest various degrees of conflict from the outset as a result of their pre-existing attitudes and experiences (Hammond, personal communication). This more relaxed technique, which approximates to real-life experience much more closely, is clearly worth further exploration, particularly in relation to the influence of drugs.

SUMMARY

In two cross-over experiments each finally employing 12 pairs of first-year preclinical medical students, the effects of alcohol upon certain measures of interpersonal "conflict" were studied in the laboratory. Four personality inventories were also completed by all subjects on both occasions. No simple or consistent relationships were observed between measures of conflict and of personality, though the former varied considerably between the first and second sessions, whereas the latter (with the possible exception of "divergence" in the second experiment) were, as expected, extremely stable. Variation in the conflict measures between sessions could not confidently be attributed to the presence or absence of alcohol, since some results from the two experiments, though unlikely to have been due to chance, were in opposite directions. This suggests that in future studies members of experimental pairs should be selected by maximizing or minimizing personality variables of interest, rather than by the degree of conflict that they demonstrate under control conditions.

Acknowledgements

We are grateful to our 60 subjects, to the Medical Research Council and to the United States Public Health Services (Grant RF 045) for financial support to C.R.B.J., and above all to Dr K. R. Hammond, for advice and help throughout, for introducing us to his quantitative technique for the study of some aspects of personal interactions in the first place, and for enabling the measures of conflict to be computed from the raw scores so rapidly.

REFERENCES

ADORNO, T. W., FRENKEL-BRUNSWICK, E., LEVISON, D. J., and SANFORD, R. N. (1950). *The Authoritarian Personality*. New York: Harper.

BONAIUTO, P., and BARTOLI, G. (1970). In *Entspannung—neue therapeutische Aspekte*, pp. 82–87, ed. Adams, C., Jochum, W., Kaech, R., Ludwig, R., and Philips, H. D. Basel: *CIBA* AG.

DAVIS, W. (1968). *Three Years' Hard Labour: The Road to Devaluation.* London: Deutsch.

EYSENCK, H. J. (ed.) (1963). *Experiments with Drugs.* Oxford: Pergamon.

FAIRLEY, P. (1966). *Are we asking too much of our statesmen? Evening Standard,* Nov. 11th., p. 10.

GETZELS, J. W., and JACKSON, P. W. (1962). *Creativity and Intelligence.* New York: Wiley.

HAMMOND, K. R. (1965). *J. soc. Issues*, **21**, 44–65.

HAMMOND, K. R., BONAIUTO, G. B., FAUCHEUX, C., MOSCOVICI, S., FRÖHLICH, W. D., JOYCE, C. R. B., and DI MAJO, G. (1968). *Int. J. Psychol.*, **3**, 1–12.

HUDSON, L. (1962). *Nature, Lond.*, **196**, 601.

JOYCE, C. R. B. (1965). In *Principles of Treatments of Psychosomatic Disorders*, pp. 23–31, ed. Hopkins, P., and Wolff, H. H. Oxford: Pergamon.

JOYCE, C. R. B., HAMMOND, K. R., PAN, L., and VARONOS, D. D. (1968). *Naunyn-Schmiedeburgs Arch. exp. Path. Pharmak.*, **259**, 180–181.

JOYCE, C. R. B., and HUDSON, L. (1968). *Br. J. med. Educ.*, **2**, 28–32.

MORAN, C. (1966). *Winston Churchill: the Struggle for Survival 1940–1965.* London: Constable.

SAKODA, J. M., COHEN, B. H., and BEALL, G. (1954). *Psychol. Bull.*, **51**, 172–175.

DISCUSSION

Boyland: Were all your subjects social drinkers?

Joyce: They were all early medical students so they were neither teetotal nor heavy-drinkers.

Silverman: As your training programme was political, did their preconceived political ideas enter into their discussion?

Joyce: I do not think so. Information was given and they were asked to predict the political progress of twenty anonymous and in fact imaginary countries.

Silverman: At the end of the experiment did they still believe that the information they had been given was important?

Joyce: Subjects found the test stimulating and meaningful. They were of course "de-briefed" at the end of the experiment.

Tomkiewicz: Did you have an independent measure of changes in attitudes within the dyads between the two trials?

Joyce: The really interesting question, which we would like to follow up, is what happens when you put, say, an authoritarian subject with a submissive one, or a convergent with a divergent. Bonaiuto and Bartoli (1970) showed the effect of benzoctamine on the ability to solve exactly the same kind of problem in neurotics. The results suggest that benzoctamine enabled the neurotics to reach agreement which is real agreement, in the sense that they admit it privately afterwards, as well as expressing it promptly.

Marley: The reduction in "conflict scores" may have been due to a practice effect. This possibility could be evaluated by repeating the tests after four weeks in one group not given alcohol and in another given alcohol on the two occasions.

Joyce: In the first experiment of the two we thought we had a practice effect but this was not so; it was just that there was less conflict on the second occasion. In the second experiment, however, there was more conflict on the second occasion than on the first.

Weiskrantz: Were some subjects just disappointed at not receiving alcohol?

Joyce: Every subject and every pair had alcohol on one of the two occasions on which they were tested.

Boyland: Were the controls given a placebo?

Joyce: No, for the reasons that I explained.

Boyland: Would it not be possible to give the controls alcohol-free drinks?

Joyce: We have tried many mixtures. None of them is satisfactory in that the subjects' guesses as to whether they have received alcohol or control are no better than would occur by chance.

Albert: What was the explanation for your findings?

Joyce: I would put it very cautiously. Our results were not inconsistent with the idea that pairs given alcohol first show more conflict four weeks later, when alcohol was not given, than those given alcohol second.

Beckett: Did the duration of the test depend upon the circumstances ? Could it have been as long as an hour ?

Joyce: Yes, it was two and a half hours or three hours in some cases.

Beckett: You gave a double whisky on an empty stomach ?

Joyce: Vodka, two hours after the last meal.

Beckett: Then there must have been very little alcohol present at the end of the test.

Joyce: Especially at the end of the experiments of long duration. I did not attempt to minimize the methodological difficulties from the pharmacological point of view. I concentrated on the sociopharmacological necessity of approximating to a real-life situation.

Weiskrantz: I understand that all subjects took part in all 20 situations. By the time they got to the 18th were they thinking that perhaps this was an experiment that was not really seriously concerned with conflict ?

Joyce: No, this is the odd thing. The first experiment we did was a non-drug experiment, simply a cross-cultural study of conflict in five or six different countries. We were convinced by this study that the subjects could be motivated to take the experiment seriously. This led us to try and repeat this work with alcohol.

Weiskrantz: What country was this done in ?

Joyce: This particular study was done in Whitechapel. A study on an English group was wanted because American and Continental groups had been investigated. The result was that the English came pretty nicely in between the other two groups.

King: Some years ago I took part in a similar study. Motivation remained high all the way through, even though we were simulating a situation.

Boyland: Did you investigate the effect of smoking in this situation ?

Joyce: No.

Beckett: The effect of alcohol depends on the blood concentration, that is, a slight improvement in performance occurs with blood alcohol levels of up to about 20 mg per cent, whereas at 40 mg per cent one can demonstrate a definite impairment of judgment.

Joyce: That is absolutely right, but it is a question of which of the many factors in a multifactorial situation one wishes to pick out. We wanted to stay close to the real-life situation.

Steinberg: What was the longest interval between your experiments?

Joyce: The interval was always four weeks.

Steinberg: One wonders how much longer the carry-over effects would last. In some of our work with psychoactive drugs in rats we detected carry-over effects after as long as three months, which in rats is a very long time indeed (Rushton, Steinberg and Tomkiewicz, 1968).

Joyce: In early learning or handling experiments the effects are lifelong.

Steinberg: Yes. But the carry-over effects we found were obtained with animals which had their first drug experience when they were already adult.

Joyce: Drugs may be more powerful modifiers of behaviour than handling. It would be surprising if, with appropriate and sensitive tests, one could *not* show long-lasting effects in man.

REFERENCES

BONAIUTO, P., and BARTOLI, G. (1970). In *Entspannung—neue therapeutische Aspekte*, pp. 82–87, ed. Adams, C., Jochum, W., Kaech, R., Ludwig, R., and Philips, H. D. Basel: *CIBA* AG.

RUSHTON, R., STEINBERG, H., and TOMKIEWICZ, M. (1968). *Nature, Lond.*, **220**, 885–889.

PHEROMONES, GROWTH AND BEHAVIOUR

J. J. Cowley and D. R. Wise

Department of Psychology, The Queen's University, Belfast

The chemicals secreted by an animal may effect the behaviour and physiology of another individual of the same species. Such substances, which act as messengers between individuals, were referred to by Bethe (1932) in relation to the sex attractants in insects as ectohormones. Karlson and Butenandt (1959) proposed the adoption of the term pheromone, and Kalmus (1964) has modified their definition to read "pheromones are substances, or mixtures of substances, which are produced by an individual and received by a second individual of the same species, in which they produce one or several specific actions". The term is used to cover chemical communications in all animals and it makes no reference to the source of the chemicals or to the structures on which they act. Olfactorily acting pheromones have received most attention, though ingestion and body contact may also provide pathways for their action. Young locusts mature more rapidly in the presence of adults; they receive the pheromone through absorption over the whole body and through the antennae (Loher, 1960). An orally active pheromone produced by the mandibular gland of the queen bee has been described and synthesized by Butler, Callow and Johnston (1961). The pheromone, "queen substance" (9-oxodecenoic acid), inhibits the development of the ovaries of workers, it is spread through the colony by workers who lick it from the body of the queen and also share it in regurgitated food with other members (Butler, 1956).

The classification of pheromones by their mode of action is but one of several classificatory systems in use. Butler (1967) used a system which depends on the biological function that the particular pheromone serves. The most extensive group is that of the olfactory sex attractants. These are produced mainly by females and attract males, though the virgin female of the Douglas fir beetle, *Dendroctonus pseudosugae* (Hopkins), has been shown by Rudinsky (1963) to produce a scent that is attractive to both sexes, and in the scorpion fly, *Harpobittacus australis* and *H. nigriceps* it is the males that produce a scent that attracts females (Bornemissza, 1964).

Olfactory pheromones in insects may act as alerting substances, as a means of aggregating members of the same species, and as aphrodisiacs. The latter, often produced by the male, may initiate a necessary part of the sexual behaviour pattern prior to successful copulation. Aphrodisiacs are known in many winged insects including butterflies. They act through the olfactory organs. In a separate category are the trail-marking pheromones used extensively in ants and termites (terrestrial trails) but also present in flying insects (aerial trails).

Wilson distinguished between pheromones that produced an immediate and reversible change in the behaviour of the recipient—the classical stimulus response pattern—and those that induce a slower but more persistent change in the endocrine and reproduction systems (Wilson and Bossert, 1963). The former he describes as releaser pheromones, while the latter, in so far as the body is "primed" for action, he referred to as primer pheromones. The expression of behaviour, consequent upon the priming, is dependent on new external stimuli, though the behaviour may occur *in vacuo* as a result of internal stimuli. A pheromone may act as both a primer and a releaser; queen substance acts as a sex attractant to the drone during the nuptial flight (releaser effect) and also retards oogenesis (primer effect).

The releaser effect has been studied extensively in insects (see reviews by Wilson and Bossert, 1963; Butler 1963). Less attention has been paid to the primer effect and to long-term changes in growth, maturation, and behaviour.

RELEASER PHEROMONES IN MAMMALS

In mammals, releaser pheromones have been implicated in a number of studies on sexual and aggressive behaviour. Removal of the olfactory bulbs may disturb receptivity in female mice (Whitten, 1956a) and guinea pigs (Donovan and Kopriva, 1965). Lamond (1959) observed a reduction in the number of oestrus cycles in anosmic mice, and Franck (1966) has shown that adult rabbits rendered anosmic before puberty fail to show sexual behaviour.

Oestrous cats introduced into a cage previously occupied by an active male display the same characteristic posturing, rolling and rubbing that they would show in the presence of the male. The behaviour is absent, however, if the cage is washed with disinfectant (Michael and Kerverne, 1968). The male ferret shows signs of agitation—increased activity and vocalization—when introduced into an open-field previously occupied by a female in late oestrus (Cowley, unpublished observation).

Studies on domestic animals confirm the importance of olfactory signals in eliciting sexual responses. The odour of the boar plays a major role, together with sound, in evoking the immobilization reflex which enables copulation to take place (Signoret and Du Mesnil du Buisson, 1961). Hart, Mead and Regan (1946) have described the role of olfactory signals in facilitating the collection of semen in bulls. From laboratory studies there is evidence that rats utilize olfactory cues both to discriminate between the sexes and between those on heat and those which are not receptive (Le Magnen, 1952).

The most striking demonstration of a pheromone releaser effect is provided by the work of Ropartz on aggression in mice. Anosmic mice (Ropartz, 1967a) flee or adopt a submissive posture when attacked by intact males, while aggressive behaviour can be elicited from mice normally living peacefully together by anointing one with urine from a strange male (Mackintosh and Grant, 1966), but if the odour of the mice is masked by an artificial perfume a delay in fighting occurs. The length of the delay is presumably dependent on the decay in perfume strength and the perception of normal mouse odour.

Ropartz (1967b) considers that male mice living in close contact with each other produce a "group odour" which is contained in the urine and produced by the coagulating glands. Fresh urine, and urine from recently castrated mice, will produce an increase in mouse activity, whereas urine from mice castrated a month before exposure is without effect (Ropartz, 1967c). A second pheromone, secreted by the pads of the feet of male mice, provides for individual identity.

Primer pheromones have been shown to have a profound effect on the reproductive behaviour of a number of mammals (see review by Bruce, 1967). Schinkel (1954) and Shelton and Morrow (1965) have observed that the introduction of the ram towards the end of anoestrus can accelerate the onset of oestrus in the ewe; the stimulus appears to be effective only under these conditions and not when the ram is run continuously with the ewes.

Control of oestrus by male sex pheromones has been demonstrated in the laboratory mouse by Whitten (1956b, 1957, 1958), and more recently in the deer mouse *Peromyscus* (Eleftheriou, Bronson and Zarrow, 1962) and in the field vole *Microtus* (Clulow and Clarke, 1968). The regular oestrus cycle which is characteristic of the rat and the hamster is absent in the mouse, except in the presence of the male when the cycle becomes shorter and more regular. The pheromone responsible has not been characterized, though it is known to be air-borne (Whitten, Bronson and Greenstein, 1968); to be effective the male must be present for forty-eight hours after the start of metoestrus (Whitten 1958). The synchronization of oestrus, known as the Whitten effect, can readily be demonstrated in the laboratory by housing female mice together for a period of 10 to 15 days and then housing them with male mice. In these conditions a maximum incidence of mating occurs on the third night after the introduction of the male.

Female mice that have been housed in an all-female environment and are then isolated for two days will also show synchronization of oestrus on the first night after pairing (Marsden and Bronson, 1965).

The results indicate that in all-female groups there is a mutual suppression of oestrus (Whitten, 1958) and that the isolation of the females provides the conditions necessary for the removal of the suppressing effects. In the Whitten effect there is an active initiation of a new cycle because of the presence of the urine of the male.

Bruce (1959, 1960) demonstrated that exposing newly mated female mice to a strange (alien) male produces a block to pregnancy. The same effect can be produced by housing the female in a cage soiled by males (Parkes and Bruce, 1962). Anosmic mice (Bruce and Parrott, 1960) do not show the block to pregnancy (Bruce effect), and castrated alien mice are ineffective in producing the block. Failure to conceive thus depends on the presence of pheromones in the male urine which are under the control of the gonads.

148   J. J. COWLEY AND D. R. WISE

The administration of prolactin prevents the failure of im-
plantation (Dominic, 1966a). Pregnancies from postpartum
conception are not blocked if lactation has been established
(Bruce and Parkes, 1961) or if an ectopic pituitary graft is present
(Dominic 1966b). These studies provide evidence for the view that
in the Bruce effect there is a failure of luteotrophic secretion which
would normally follow mating and, arising from this failure, the
corpora lutea of ovulation do not develop into those of pregnancy
or pseudopregnancy (Parkes, 1961).

RELEASER PHEROMONES IN PRIMATES

The primer effect of pheromones has not been studied in the
primates, though there is ample evidence to suggest that in many
species olfaction acts as a means of communication between the
sexes. Petter (1965) observed marking in the lemurs of Madagas-
car. A number of species in the sub-family *Lemurinae* have
glands on the forearm and at the level of the armpit the secretions
of which are used to mark branches. In *Lemur catta*, the female
marks objects with the clitoris, while other species use their hands
or the top of their heads to mark with urine or excrement.

In many prosimians, sweat and sebaceous glands are numerous
on the face, feet and genital regions (Montagna, 1962), and Marler
(1965) considers that these may serve an olfactory function.

Monkeys smell the ano-genital region and variations in the
behaviour of male rhesus monkeys have been related to rhythmic
changes in the menstrual cycle of female partners with which they
were paired (Michael, Saayman and Zumpe, 1967). The behavioural fluctuations are lost with ovariectomy but they can
be restored by injecting ovarian hormones into the female
(Michael, Herbert and Welegalla, 1967). Operant conditioning
experiments have provided additional evidence that the male
responds to odours associated with the female cycle; a male
rhesus monkey will press a lever to gain access to an oestrogenized
female, but will not do so for anhormonal females (Michael and
Keverne, 1968). More recently Michael and Keverne (1970)
have shown that oestrogen-stimulated vaginal secretions (copulin)
are able to activate male interest in the female (lever-pressing)
and overt sexual behaviour (mounting and ejaculation).

In chimpanzees Lawick-Goodall (1968) observed frequent
inspection by males of the female genitalia and that changes in

swelling and deturgescence are associated with an increase in attractiveness to the males. The relative parts played by olfactory, tactile and visual information in eliciting behaviour remain to be determined. Pheromones have not been shown to be present in man, but there is evidence which suggests that he is able to detect olfactory stimuli associated with the oestrus cycle of other species as well as his own. Jay (1965) reported the presence of a strong-smelling discharge during certain days of the menstrual cycle of toque macaques, and the olfactory acuity of young women to exaltolide is known to vary with particular times of the menstrual cycle (Vierling and Rock, 1967).

In man the odour of perspiration varies with the location of the sweat and sebaceous glands, and there are more sweat glands on the bottom of the hand and the top of the foot than any other part of the body (Barail, 1947). Diet may contribute to a change in the chemical composition of perspiration (Barail, 1946), and ethnic groups are known to vary in the amount of sweat they produce (McCance and Purohit, 1969).

PHEROMONES IN DEVELOPMENT

The role of pheromones in growth and development has received little attention. Reference has already been made to the work on locusts and to the part played by queen substance in suppressing oogenesis. Our work has been directed to the part played by pheromones in changing the pace of development of mice and to an appraisal of the interaction of releaser and primer effects in modifying the activity of rats and mice.

Vandenbergh (1967) reared female mice in a cage with a mature male, either from day two to 21 or from day 21 to 40 after birth and found no marked differences in body weight between these mice and those reared without the presence of a male. Rather different results were obtained from a study controlled by Fullerton and Cowley (1970) in which infant female mice and their mothers were housed in metal shoe-box-type cages which were contained in a larger cage. In the latter, either free-running male or adult female mice were able to scamper over the wire mesh lids of the boxes housing the mothers and their litters. The mice exposed to the adult males grew more rapidly than those exposed to the female mice, and there were significant differences

in body weight at 21 days, when the mice were weaned, and at
40 days of age (Fig. 1).

In a second experiment we followed much the same procedure;
again mice exposed to males showed accelerated development
during the pre-weaning period. In both experiments the mothers,
and the young from the time they left the nest, could make body

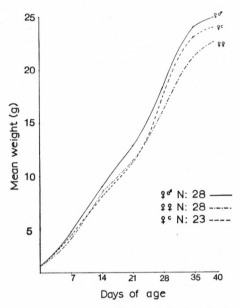

FIG. 1. Changes in the mean body weights from birth to 40
days of female mice exposed to the presence of adult male
and female mice.

contact with the free-running mice through the grids of the shoe-
box cages. Also waste products from the adult mice could pass
into the smaller cages.

In so far as the mice that were exposed to the presence of the
females were somewhat lighter at 40 days of age than the control
mice, it would seem that the proximity of the mature mice
exercised a differential effect on the growth of the young.

Female mice housed in groups of 30 did not differ significantly
in body weight from mice housed individually. The ovaries of the

grouped mice were, however, lighter and corpora lutea were either absent or atrophic (Whitten, 1959). Elsewhere Whitten (1957) has reported a reduction in the weight of the uterus of grouped mice.

Ropartz (1969) has recently shown that exposing mice to an air current containing the odour of adult male and female mice, produces hypertrophy of the uterus. Terman (1968) has similarly reported an increase in the weight of the uterus of prairie deermice (*Peromyscus maniculatus bairdii*) after exposure to soiled bedding taken from an asymptotic population of the same mice. An increase in population density produces atrophy of the gonads and these findings of Christian (1959) may well reflect on common elements in the situations. The inconsistency of the findings on total body weight changes do not enable us to draw firm conclusions. However, a number of studies show that the exposure of female mice to the presence of an adult male accelerates sexual development. Thus, caging a male with a lactating mother and her young or introducing an adult male after the young are weaned accelerates sexual development as shown by the early onset of first oestrus (Vandenbergh, 1967). Also the acceleration is related to the length of time the male is present and affects both the age at which the vagina opens and first mating occurs.

Introducing an adult female mouse every third day also accelerated the onset of oestrus, though not to the same extent as exposing the mice to a new adult male every third day. Vandenbergh (1969) has shown that it is the odour of the male mouse that is responsible for the acceleration and that odours from males caged in proximity to oestrous females are more effective as activators than those of males housed alone.

Early maturation of sexual development was also observed when young female mice were exposed from birth to the presence of adult male mice. In these studies (Fullerton and Cowley, 1970) the presence of the adult males accelerated the pace of general somatic development as judged by the age at which the eyes and auditory canal opened, the lower incisors erupted, and "full-fur" was reached. Functional changes accompanied the changes in growth. Thus, the mice exposed to the adult males responded to a sharp sound at an earlier age than either the controls on mice exposed to females. There were no marked differences in somatic

6

or functional development between the mice exposed to the presence of adult females and the control mice other than in sexual development. Vaginal introitus and first oestrus were delayed in these mice.

Castro (1967) has reported that mice weaned at 21 days of age and housed with mature males show early vagina opening. In a

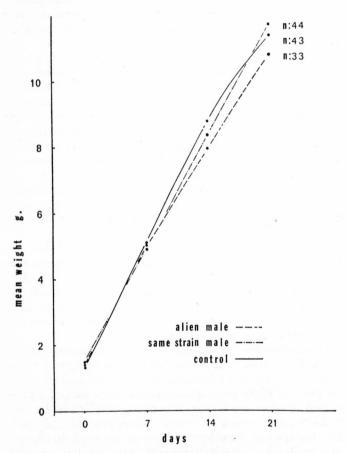

FIG. 2. Differences in growth rates between female mice exposed to male mice of the same strain (TO) and those exposed to males of an alien (CS1) strain.

second experiment a linear relationship was observed between the number of female mice caged together and the age the vagina opened; the larger the number of females the greater the delay in maturation.

The block to pregnancy which occurs when a recently-mated female mouse is exposed to the presence of an alien male has encouraged us to investigate whether the presence of a male from an alien strain would differentially affect the growth of young mice. In these experiments three males were housed in cylindrical cages some distance above the shoe-box-type cages which house the mother and her litter. Food-spill and waste products from the males fall into the cages of the mothers, but the males cannot make direct body contact with them or their offspring. If, in this situation, female mice of the CS1 strain are exposed to the presence of males of another albino strain (TO) then the pace of their development, as assessed by the increase in body weight, is somewhat slower. The differences in body weight are not large, but they have been consistent in a number of studies (Fig. 2).

The genotype of the mother and the young contribute to the post-natal growth of mice (Brumby 1960). The present experiments suggest that growth and development may be modified by exposure to members of the same and alien strains.

INFANT RAT ACTIVITY

The presence of soiled bedding, taken from the cage in which the mother is suckling her litter, has an effect on the movement of young rats at an early age.

In one experiment baby rats were removed from their mothers at five, seven or nine days of age and their movements recorded by giving a point for each sideways or vertical movement of the head and trunk and for any flexion of the limbs. These arbitrary "activity units" were recorded for a two-minute period in an "oven" with a perspex door at a temperature of 30°C ($\pm 2°$). Half the litter was tested with soiled sawdust present and half with stock sawdust. The sawdust is placed in a raised trough and the rats do not have direct access to it. All rats were only tested once in these conditions.

Age and activity

The activity of the seven and nine day old rats in the presence of the stock sawdust was the same. When the rats were tested in the presence of the *home-cage sawdust* they showed less activity

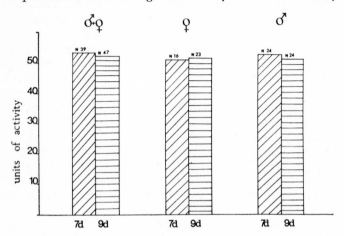

mean scores 7 and 9 days of age

FIG. 3. Changes in infant rat activity on days 7 and 9 in the presence of stock sawdust (control conditions).

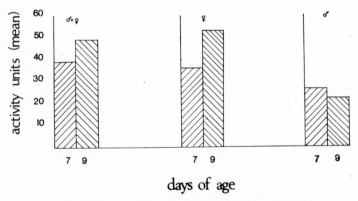

days of age

FIG. 4. Changes in infant rat activity on days 7 and 9 in the presence of home-cage sawdust. The increase in activity is entirely due to an increase in the activity of the females.

on day seven than they did on day nine. The increase in activity from day seven to day nine was entirely due to an increase in the activity of the females ($P < 0.02$). The males showed a slight, though not significant, decrease in activity (Figs. 3 and 4).

Sex differences in activity

On day nine (Fig. 5) the activity of the males was less than that of the females when tested in the presence of the soiled sawdust ($P < 0.04$). The females were as active at this stage as the control rats of the same age.

Treatment differences

There was some evidence that at seven days of age the rats showed less activity in the presence of the soiled sawdust ($P < 0.02$). The direction was the same for both males and females though an acceptable level of statistical significance was not

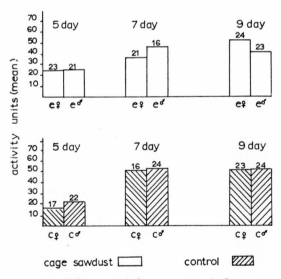

FIG. 5. Sex differences in infant rat activity in the presence of soiled and stock sawdust on days 5, 7 and 9 after birth. The males are less active on day 9 than the females. The activity has been recorded for two minutes at a constant temperature.

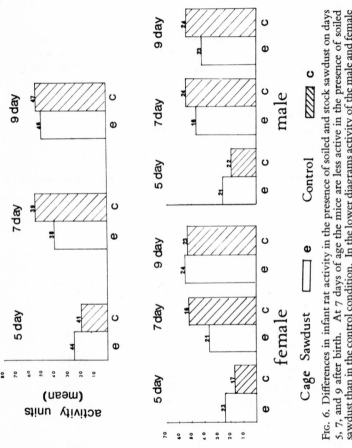

FIG. 6. Differences in infant rat activity in the presence of soiled and stock sawdust on days 5, 7, and 9 after birth. At 7 days of age the mice are less active in the presence of soiled sawdust than in the control condition. In the lower diagrams activity of the male and female mice is shown separately.

maintained when the groups were divided on the basis of sex (Fig. 6).

In a second experiment we counted the number of squares drawn on a grid that the baby rat traversed in a two-minute period. The rats were tested on alternate days from the second day after birth; again each rat was tested only once. In this experiment the litters were left with the mother until the babies were removed one at a time for testing. In place of the soiled sawdust, urine collected from a lactating mother was used. At six days of age rats tested in the presence of the urine were less active than those tested in the presence of water ($P < 0.005$); this reduced activity was noticeable in both the male and female rats, though at a less significant level ($P < 0.05$). The results of the second experiment were essentially similar to the first and indicate that within the first 10 days of birth the rats react differently to the presence of stock sawdust as compared with the presence of soiled sawdust or urine from a lactating mother, and male and female babies react differently.

RAT WHEEL ACTIVITY

The presence of urine from an adult rat can modify the wheel running activity of a recipient, and the effect varies with the reproductive state of the activator. In these experiments two conventional activity wheels were housed side-by-side at a distance of about 60 cm from each other. Forty-five cm above each wheel a female rat was housed in a cylindrical cage with a funnel shaped bottom and a wire-mesh floor and top. The urine from these rats was fed down to an area immediately below the wheel so that the recipient did not have access to it. During the preliminary period of adaptation (4–6 weeks) urine was not filtered to the base of the wheel. One rat acted as a control for the other.

Fig. 7 shows the effects of the presence of the urine of a normal rat on wheel running activity. The regular four-day cycle of activity was continued with the level of activity slightly reduced after exposure to the urine. Discontinuing the presence of the urine eventually produced a more marked change in the cycle of activity, and the peak of activity was delayed by 24 hours. In neither case did we observe any shortening of vaginal oestrus.

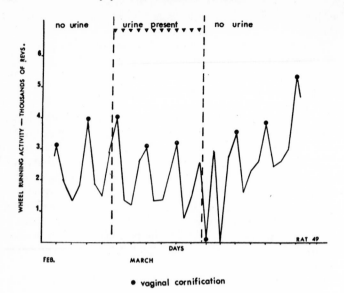

FIG. 7. The effect of female urine on wheel running activity in albino rats. Exposure to the urine of a normal female rat does not alter the cycle of activity, though the level of activity may be slightly reduced. Removal of the urine delays the peak of activity, though not vaginal cornification.

When the activator has been mated and returned to her cage marked changes in the wheel running activity of the recipient rat occurred within some hours of mating. Wheel running activity was not only reduced but the regular cell changes in vaginal epithelium were no longer apparent. Two examples of the type of change that occur are shown in Fig. 8. In both instances the rat was exposed to the urine the day after oestrus which reduced the amount of activity and shortened the length of the next cycle. The regular synchronization of oestrus and the activity peaks were lost and the rat showed constant cornification and a considerable increase in activity after exposure to the urine for 10 to 12 days. When the rat was mated, but not made pregnant, there was a lowering of activity but no change in the vaginal cell cycle (Fig. 9). This is similar to the condition shown in Fig. 7.

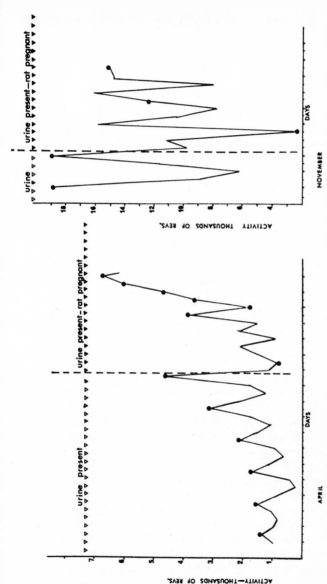

FIG. 8. Activity following exposure to a pregnant rat. Exposure to the urine within some hours of mating the activator shortens the length of the cycle as shown by changes in vaginal cornification. In both rats, following exposure, a reduction in activity occurs. Synchronization of activity and vaginal cornification is no longer apparent.

6*

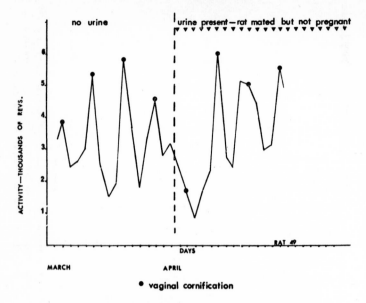

FIG. 9. Activity following exposure to the urine of a rat which
has been mated but is not pregnant. The level of activity
is lowered but there is no change in the length of the vaginal
cycle.

Fig. 10 shows the change in wheel activity when the rat was
exposed to the urine of late pregnancy and post-parturition.
Before the birth of the young the recipient, which is in constant
oestrus, shows a transitory fall in activity. The lower figure
shows the change in wheel activity that occurs when the urine from
the same lactating rats is transferred to the control rat which has,
up to this point in time, been exposed to the urine of a non-
pregnant female. An increase in activity occurs but there is no
change in the length of the vaginal cycle.

The illustrations (Figs. 7 to 10) have been selected from the
records of two rats over a four-month period. We tested other
animals but our numbers remain small and we have no idea
how much variation there might be. All animals were tested
in isolation from other members of the colony. Though we
may have to qualify our findings it appears that exposure of a

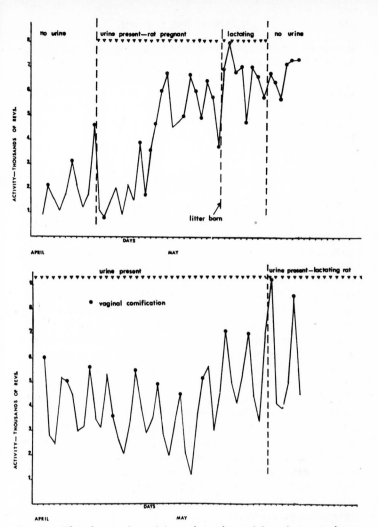

FIG. 10. The changes in activity when the recipient is exposed to the urine of a pregnant and lactating rat (top record). The rat, which is in constant oestrus, shows a transitory fall in activity prior to the birth of the litter and this is followed by an increase in activity during the period when the activator is lactating.

Urine from the same lactating mother is filtered to a second recipient which had, up to that time, been exposed to the urine of a normal rat (lower record). The exposure is accompanied by an increase in the peaks of wheel running activity, but the length of the cycle remains unchanged.

female rat to the urine of another female rat may modify behavioural oestrus and the cyclic vaginal changes.

In the studies of both infant rat activity and of wheel running the rats did not have access to the urine and it seems likely that the changes are produced by stimuli of an olfactory nature. Though they appear to act rapidly on the recipient they may well produce changes which are permanent.

ACTIVITY IN OPEN–FIELD TEST

Restricting the movements of young male mice with a polythene ruff-like collar reduced their activity in the open-field, and this was still observable three to four weeks after the collars were removed. Male mice weaned late (35 and 42 days of age) also showed reduced activity in the open-field test. Thus a prolonged period with the mother in infancy reduced activity in the open-field situation; nutrition did not appear to be important in these results (Cowley, Williamson and Berryman, 1970). Whether the restriction of movement imposed by the collar is in any way analogous to that associated with the prolonged period with the mother remains to be determined.

Infant female mice exposed to the presence of adult male mice of the same strain were more active in Hall's open-field test than the controls, though exposure in infancy to adult females had little effect on their open-field activity (Fullerton and Cowley, 1970). The number of squares entered and the number of times they stood up in the field were greater in the female mice exposed to males and they took less time than the controls to leave the section of the field (latency score) to which they were first introduced. The latency score of mice reared in proximity to the adult females was longer than that of either the male-exposed or the control mice (Fig. 11).

In the above studies the relative roles of releasing and priming effects remain to be determined. The changes in activity during infancy in the presence of soiled sawdust and the modification of adult wheel running activity represent examples of immediate effects. But in the mouse, structural and functional changes occur in the first few days after birth and these are associated with a modification in the behaviour of the adult.

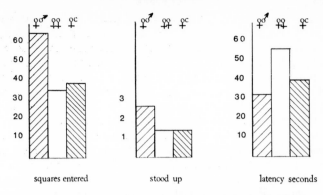

FIG. 11. Differences in open-field behaviour in female mice exposed in infancy to the presence of adult males and females. The figure shows the mean difference in the number of squares entered and in the frequency of standing up. The mean time (seconds) that the mice remained in the area where first introduced (latency) is greater for mice exposed to the presence of females; male-exposed mice stood up and entered more squares in the test.

SUMMARY

Pheromones have been shown to have a marked effect on the behaviour of animals as disparate as the social insects and monkeys. Their role in the reproductive behaviour of the mouse has been well documented and there is much to suggest that they also play a critical part in the mating behaviour of certain mammals. As they act on the central nervous system and on neurohumoral pathways their effects, in the mouse, may be immediate, as exemplified by studies of induced aggression, or their action may be delayed as in the block to pregnancy (Bruce effect). While there is extensive literature on the part played by pheromones in reproductive and social behaviour, little attention has been given to their growth-promoting properties. Accelerated sexual development occurs when young female mice are exposed to the presence of adult male mice, and there is some suggestion that exposure to adult female mice may also affect growth and maturation. The pheromones responsible for these changes are unknown but they appear to be active during infancy and the post-weaning period. They are also associated with a modification of open-field behaviour when the mice are tested as adults. Activity in infant rats is modified by the presence of soiled bedding from the home cage, and by the urine of a lactating rat. Exposure to the urine of an adult female rat may have an effect on wheel running activity and the reproductive state of the activator is implicated in these changes. The behavioural changes in the infant and adult rats are regarded as indicative of the presence of olfactorily acting stimuli that have an immediate releasing effect, while the change in the pace of development of the mice provides evidence of a more persistent effect which also finds expression in the open-field behaviour. The releaser and primer effects act at an early age but whether from a common source is not known.

REFERENCES

BARAIL, L. C. (1946). *Rayon Text. Mon.*, **27**, 663–666.
BARAIL, L. C. (1947). *Rayon Text. Mon.*, **28**, 93–97.
BETHE, A. (1932). *Naturwissenschaften*, **20**, 177–181.
BORNEMISSZA, G. F. (1964). *Nature, Lond.*, **203**, 786–787.
BRUCE, H. M. (1959). *Nature, Lond.*, **184**, 105.
BRUCE, H. M. (1960). *J. Reprod. Fertil.*, **1**, 96–103.
BRUCE, H. M. (1967). *Ciba Fdn Study Grp The Effect of External Stimuli on Reproduction*, pp. 29–42. London: Churchill.
BRUCE, H. M., and PARKES, A. S. (1961). *J. Endocr.*, **22**, vi–vii.
BRUCE, H. M., and PARROTT, D. M. V. (1960). *Science*, **131**, 1526.
BRUMBY, P. J. (1960). *Heredity, Lond.*, **14**, 1–18.
BUTLER, C. G. (1956). *Proc. R. ent. Soc. Lond., A*, **31**, 12–16.
BUTLER, C. G. (1963). In *Insect Reproduction*, pp. 66–77, ed. Highman, K. C. Symposium No. 2, Royal Entomological Society, London.
BUTLER, C. G. (1967). *Biol. Rev.*, **42**, 42–87.
BUTLER, C. G., CALLOW, R. K., and JOHNSTON, N. C. (1961). *Proc. R. Soc., B*, **155**, 417–431.
CASTRO, B. M. (1967). *Anais Acad. bras. Cient.*, **39**, 289–291.
CHRISTIAN, J. J. (1959). In *Comparative Endocrinology* (Proceedings of Columbia University Symposium), pp. 71–97, ed. Gorbman, A. New York: Wiley.
CLULOW, F. V., and CLARKE, J. R. (1968). *Nature, Lond.*, **219**, 511.
COWLEY, J. J., WILLIAMSON, A. J., and BERRYMAN, J. C. (1970). *Proc. VIII Int. Congr. Nutr.* Prague. Amsterdam: Excerpta Medica Foundation.
DOMINIC, C. J. (1966a). *J. Reprod. Fertil.*, **11**, 407–414.
DOMINIC, C. J. (1966b). *J. Reprod. Fertil.*, **11**, 415–421.
DONOVAN, B. T., and KOPRIVA, P. C. (1965). *Endocrinology*, **77**, 213–217.

ELEFTHERIOU, B. E., BRONSON, F. H., and ZARROW, M. X. (1962). *Science*, **137,** 764.

FRANCK, H. (1966). *C. r. Séanc. Soc. Biol.*, **160,** 389–391.

FULLERTON, C. E. O., and COWLEY, J. J. (1970). *J. genet. Psychol.*, in press.

HART, G. H., MEAD, S. W., and REGAN, W. M. (1946). *Endocrinology*, **39,** 221–223.

JAY, P. (1965). In *Behaviour of Nonhuman Primates*, pp. 525–591, ed. Schrier, A. M. New York: Academic Press.

KALMUS, H. (1964). *Proc. II int. Cong. Endocr.*, pt. 1, pp. 188–192. London: Academic Press.

KARLSON, P., and BUTENANDT, A. (1959). *A. Rev. Ent.*, **4,** 39–58.

LAMOND, D. R. (1959). *J. Endocr.*, **18,** 343–349.

LAWICK-GOODALL, J. VAN (1968). *Anim. Behav. Monogr.*, **1(3),** 161–311.

LE MAGNEN, J. (1952). *Archs. Sci. physiol.*, **6,** 295.

LOHER, W. (1960). *Proc. R. Soc., B*, **153,** 380–397.

McCANCE, R. A., and PUROHIT, G. (1969). *Nature, Lond.*, **221,** 378–379.

MACKINTOSH, J. H., and GRANT, E. C. (1966). *Z. Tierpsychol.*, **23,** 584–587.

MARLER, P. (1965). In *Primate Behaviour*, pp. 544–584, ed. DeVore, I. New York: Holt, Rinehart and Winston.

MARSDEN, H. M., and BRONSON, F. H. (1965). *J. Endocr.*, **32,** 313–319.

MICHAEL, R. P., HERBERT, J., and WELEGALLA, J. (1967). *J. Endocr.*, **39,** 81–98.

MICHAEL, R. P., and KEVERNE, E. B. (1968). *Nature, Lond.*, **218,** 746–749.

MICHAEL, R. P., and KEVERNE, E. B. (1970). *Nature, Lond.*, **225,** 84–85.

MICHAEL, R. P., SAAYMAN, G. S., and ZUMPE, D. (1967). *Nature, Lond.*, **215,** 554–556.

MONTAGNA, W. (1962). *Ann. N.Y. Acad. Sci.*, **102,** 190–209.

PARKES, A. S. (1961). In *Proc. IV Int. Congr. Anim. Reprod.*, vol. 2, pp. 163–165. The Hague.

PARKES, A. S., and BRUCE, H. M. (1962). *J. Reprod. Fertil.*, **4,** 303–308.

PETTER, J. J. (1965). In *Primate Behaviour*, pp. 292–319, ed. DeVore, I. New York: Holt, Rinehart and Winston.

ROPARTZ, P. (1967a). *Rev. Comp. Animal*, **2,** 97–102.

ROPARTZ, P. (1967b). *Colloques int. Cent. natn. Rech. scient.*, No. 173, 1.

ROPARTZ, P. (1967c). *Rev. Comp. Animal*, **4,** 71–82.

ROPARTZ, P. (1969). *C. r. hebd. Séanc. Acad. Sci., Paris*, **269,** 618–619.

RUDINSKY, J. A. (1963). *Contr. Boyce Thomson Inst. Pl. Res.*, **22,** 23–38.

SCHINKEL, P. G. (1954). *Aust. vet. J.*, **30,** 189–195.

SHELTON, M., and MORROW, J. T. (1965). *J. Anim. Sci,.* **24,** 795–799.

SIGNORET, J. P., and DU MESNIL DU BUISSON, F. (1961). In *Proc. IV Int. Congr. Anim. Reprod.*, vol. 2, p. 171. The Hague.

TERMAN, C. R. (1968). *Ecology*, **49,** 1169–1172.

VANDENBERGH, J. G. (1967). *Endocrinology*, **81,** 345–349.

VANDENBERGH, J. G. (1969). *Endocrinology*, **84,** 658–660.

VIERLING, J. S., and ROCK, J. (1967). *J. appl. Physiol.*, **22,** 311–315.

WHITTEN, W. K. (1956a). *J. Endocr.*, **14,** 160–163.

WHITTEN, W. K. (1956b). *J. Endocr.*, **13,** 399–404.

WHITTEN, W. K. (1957). *Nature, Lond.*, **180,** 1436.

WHITTEN, W. K. (1958). *J. Endocr.*, **17,** 307–313.

WHITTEN, W. K. (1959). *J. Endocr.*, **18,** 102–107.

WHITTEN, W. K., BRONSON, F. H., and GREENSTEIN, J. A. (1968). *Science*, **161,** 584–585.

WILSON, E. O., and BOSSERT, W. H. (1963). *Recent Prog. Horm. Res.*, **19,** 673–710.

DISCUSSION

Boyland: Do pheromones affect appetite? Is the effect due to increased utilization of food or increased food intake?

Cowley: It is probably due to increased food intake. A number of studies have reported that stimulation in early infancy led in the rat to an increase in growth, but we have been unable to reproduce these results (Cowley and Widdowson, 1965). The change in growth observed in the pheromone studies may depend on a change in suckling.

Boyland: If this could be extended to man, hygiene would presumably affect behaviour.

Cowley: I agree.

Kety: In the experiments in which urine was run down into the lower cage, did the sex of the recipient animal affect the results?

Cowley: Both activator and recipient were female.

Kety: This implies feedback on the same animal of her own odours. What is the significance of their being the same sex?

Cowley: Do you mean "Why haven't I used the male?"?

Kety: I suppose something else would have happened with a male. But in your experiment the recipient animal must have been affected by its own endocrine state.

Cowley: Yes. But this experiment also provides a simple way of showing how a change in the reproductive state of one animal may influence the behaviour of another, presumably through olfactory pathways.

Marley: I can see how this might influence the toxicity of drugs. Hardinge and Peterson (1963) demonstrated that the much greater lethality of amphetamine for grouped than for isolated mice was not due so much to "aggregation" but to physical activity: the greater the activity of the mice the smaller the LD_{50} for amphetamine. If simply adding "home-cage sawdust" to the group increases their activity, then the lethality of amphetamine is also likely to be enhanced.

Cowley: In an all-female group of mice atrophy of the ovaries and loss of weight of the uterus occurs (Whitten, 1957, 1959).

Albert: Did the lovelorn ferret that died in three days die of a broken heart?

Cowley: This observation was made by Miss E. M. Pinsent, who had introduced two male ferrets over a number of days into an enclosure previously occupied by females on heat. In these conditions, the males showed hyperactivity and vocalization. Both males died within a day or two of each other and a short time after exposure.

Albert: Did they stop eating?

Cowley: No, at autopsy the stomachs were full and there was no obvious cause of death.

Kety: Can pheromones operate across species? I have the impression that because I was once bitten by a laboratory rat I have a tendency to be anxious in handling them, and they appear to sense this. Is it possible that, due to my anxiety, I am exuding a pheromone?

Cowley: I do not know.

Philp: The mosquito presumably finds its meals by olfactory means. In this case the skin excretion of the human acts as a pheromone.

Cowley: These examples do not fall into the category of pheromones which are, by definition, within species, but I have no doubt that what you say about mosquitos is correct.

Philp: It is correct. Work has been done in the United States in connexion with anti-mosquito programmes (Maibach *et al.*, 1969). When air from the human forearm is presented to a particular part of the cage, the mosquitos probe there.

Cowley: Sex attractants are being used to trap insect pests. The Douglas fir beetle has been captured by using extracts of the appropriate pheromone (Rudinsky, 1963).

Beckett: Wright (1968) in British Columbia has shown that the mosquito is not necessarily attracted to the human arm, which is assumed to be giving the odour, but prefers a region with a high humidity and carbon dioxide content (such as a bit of blotting-paper).

Steinberg: Why do you define pheromones as operating only within a species?

Cowley: This is the original definition and we have kept to it.

If it were extended one would have to include a wide range of olfactorily acting substances that evoke behaviour. As early as day 1 or day 2 after exposure to Boots 365 eau de cologne, the rat shows marked motor activity (Foote, 1969). I do not know what the active agent is in this cologne.

Boyland: The main constituent is isopropyl alcohol. You might try the effect of that on these rats.

Cowley: If the rats are exposed to the perfume they leave the nest. If exposure is continued for several days the activity decreases. Normally rats do not leave the nest until they are about 14 days old. Our assumption is that the odour of the mother is blocked by the artificial perfume. Gard, Hard and Petersson (1967) have reported similar effects in the presence of ammonia.

Philp: Have you examined the reactions of mice to rats?

Cowley: No.

Philp: This might be interesting. You have defined pheromones very narrowly; it would be useful to know if there are inter-species responses.

Kety: If the olfactory tracts in a muricidal rat are cut it no longer kills mice. This suggests that the odour of the mouse is a stimulant to the rat.

Cowley: I agree that odour may provide a means of identification. When fostering or operating on very young animals we remove the mother and then place the young in the nest some time before returning the mother. This facilitates the mother's acceptance of them, presumably because they take on the nest odour.

Silverman: How specific is the olfactory sense, in relation to pheromones, on the mating behaviour of rats? Beach (1951) claimed that in the male rat deprivation of any one sense was more or less equivalent to deprivation of any other. And how specific are the pheromones? Any ongoing behaviour can be disturbed by the introduction of a strange smell.

Cowley: The rat certainly seems to be sensitive to the odour of its own environment.

Boyland: Do pheromones affect human behaviour?

Cowley: As a student of comparative behaviour, and bearing in mind the findings on monkeys already referred to, I would be surprised if they did not.

Boyland: It is remarkable how few molecules of the sex attractant are needed in insects to be effective over long distances.

Cowley: The effective range for rats and mice is limited. If two rats are housed in adjacent activity wheels, 60 cm apart, and urine is filtered down into one wheel, it is only the animal in this wheel which shows increased activity. Parkes and Bruce (1962) noted similar results when they described the Bruce effect. It was only after soil had been taken from a number of cages containing male animals that the block to pregnancy occurred.

Tomkiewicz: To what extent does the potency of the pheromones depend on the sensory acuity of a particular species? Would you, for example, get similar effects on behaviour in the bird by using visual displays since birds seem to rely so much on their eyes? Are pheromones different in principle from other systems used for transmitting information?

Cowley: I know of no specific work on birds; but what strikes one is the extraordinary range of the evolutionary scale over which the pheromones operate.

Boyland: It should be easier to investigate these effects in human subjects than in animals because people can talk.

Cowley: Mrs. A. Beard and I (unpublished observations) studied methods of selecting pupil pilots. As part of the selection procedure the candidates had to do a series of psychological tests which were individually administered by psychologists—all of whom were young women. The pupils were being treated more or less continuously over a period of several months and assessed for various qualities of temperament such as nervousness. We correlated the assessments these female psychologists gave with phases of their menstrual cycles and found good evidence that about seven days before the onset of the menses the assessors showed increased irritability with the candidates and, hence, were not able to assess them objectively.

Weiskrantz: Verbal behaviour in man does not necessarily correlate with other kinds of behaviour. But the large amount of money spent on perfumes must reflect a certain interest in olfactory stimulation.

Murphy and Schneider (1970) have found that the sexual behaviour of the male hamster is completely abolished by removal of the olfactory bulb.

Silverman: Ablation experiments, such as those of Murphy and Schneider and the older work of Beach (1951), are very crude.

We should try to find out if the pheromones are unique and specific, and if their absence could be compensated for through another sense modality.

Cowley: Animals do not only smell, they utilize any other information they can.

Silverman: If one could identify a pheromone, could one also exclude possible influences from any other compounds?

Cowley: Yes. Pheromones are specific, and about 40 have already been identified and synthesized. We also know a little about cross-species effects. If one moth attractant has a particular chemical structure, a closely related chemical substance may attract the same or an allied species.

REFERENCES

BEACH, F. A. (1951). In *Handbook of Experimental Psychology*, ed. Stevens, S. S. New York: Wiley.

COWLEY, J. J., and WIDDOWSON, E. M. (1965). *Br. J. Nutr.*, **19**, 397–406.

FOOTE, T. P. (1969). B.Sc. Thesis. The Queen's University, Belfast.

GARD, C., HARD, E., and PETERSSON, V. (1967). *Anim. Behav.*, **15**, 563–567.

HARDINGE, M. G., and PETERSON, D. I. (1963). *J. Pharmac. exp. Ther.*, **141**, 260–265.

MAIBACH, H. I., KHAN, A. A., STRAUSS, W. G., and SKINNER, W. A. (1969). *Conn. Med.*, **33**, 23–28.

MURPHY, M. R., and SCHNEIDER, G. E. (1970). *Science*, **167**, 302–303.

PARKES, A. S., and BRUCE, H. M. (1962). *J. Reprod. Fertil.*, **4**, 303–308.

RUDINSKY, J. A. (1963). *Contr. Boyce Thomson Inst. Pl. Res.*, **22**, 23–38.

WHITTEN, W. K. (1957). *Nature, Lond.*, **180**, 1436.

WHITTEN, W. K. (1959). *J. Endocr.*, **18**, 102–107.

WRIGHT, R. H. (1968). *New Scient.*, **37**, 694–697.

EXPERIMENTAL BIOLOGICAL MODELS OF NEUROTROPIC AND PSYCHOTROPIC EFFECTS OF ENVIRONMENTAL CHEMICAL AGENTS*

M. Horváth and E. Frantík

Institute of Industrial Hygiene and Occupational Diseases, Prague

Increasing numbers of new substances are being disseminated throughout the human environment. This leads to increasing the total chemical burden of the body, and arises from both involuntary exposure to environmental pollutants and deliberate consumption of substances such as drugs.

Advances in technology have reduced gross exposure to noxious chemicals and confined acute toxic effects to accidental situations and cases of hypersensitivity. But technological and social developments have increased the number of situations in which even a small and rapidly reversible chemically induced functional disturbance may lead to accidents and disease. Thus a pathological condition may be indirectly caused by chemicals. According to Smyth (1956) more than one third of the industrial chemicals listed in the American table of Threshold Limit Values affect the central nervous system (CNS) at the threshold concentration or at concentrations two- or tenfold above the recommended level.

The long-term action of low concentrations or doses, or the simultaneous action of several chemical agents, provokes rather unspecific reactions and interactions at the metabolic or regulative level; changes in central nervous function frequently dominate the clinical picture.

We cannot extrapolate back from traditional studies of mortality and morbidity to the relatively low concentrations which are likely to cause harmful effects in man (Barnes and Denz, 1954). The findings that detectable functional changes precede obvious morphological injury has led to attempts to use functional

---

* This paper could not be read at the time of the meeting.

tests to make predictions. These tests are gradually becoming a routine part of environmental and industrial toxicological studies (WHO, 1969).

It may be assumed that, apart from the direct neurotoxic effects, the chemically induced functional changes contribute to the repeated failures of adaptation to psychogenic stress, and thus to aberrant behaviour. Because the CNS is involved in many of the chemically induced pathological states, behavioural and neurophysiological models may be useful in predicting the noxious effects of low concentrations of chemicals.

The complexities involved in interpreting the results of environmental toxicological studies were expressed in the resolution of *The 2nd Symposium on Maximum Allowable Concentrations of Noxious Chemical Substances in the Working Environment* (Truhaut, 1964). It was stressed that sufficient data are not yet available to make it possible to assess the hazard of exposure to man on the basis of results gained in animals, and that differences in theoretical approach, terminology and in the interpretation of methods used in the study of nervous functions need to be resolved, particularly by comparative studies of the effects of toxic materials and values of the different techniques.

The practical importance of drug-induced impairment of psychomotor performance in relation to traffic and occupational safety has been expressed in several reports (e.g. WHO 1965, 1968). There is now international cooperation in research on the effects of drugs on the behaviour of car drivers, and Goldberg and Havard (1968) have proposed an integrated research programme.

Numerous studies have used behavioural and neurophysiological functional tests to study the deleterious effects of chemical compounds. But the results are only of limited practical value as there is a lack of rational criteria for selecting suitable experimental procedures. To test the effects of low concentrations sensitive methods have to be used, but these are generally unspecific and lack the validity of clinical and epidemiological findings and of classical toxicological effects—mortality and tissue injury.

In this paper we shall discuss our attempts to select suitable procedures for assessing the neurotropic and psychotropic action of chemicals and interpreting quantitatively the results.

EXPERIMENTAL MODELS

For a number of years our techniques have been used in two types of experimental studies (Horváth and Formánek, 1954; Horváth, 1961; Horváth et al., 1961): (a) chronic toxicity due to industrial solvents, and (b) acute effects of toxic substances and drugs on psychomotor performance in activities requiring attention or vigilance (e.g. in industry and traffic). To assess the neuro-toxic potency of chemicals a complex of testing techniques was used to provide information about the impairment of functions at various levels of complexity.

The methods and criteria usually employed in psychological and physiological research often do not possess the qualities required in tests for toxic effects, and findings may be sensitive to components of the experimental procedure, such as position, size and shape of the apparatus, and frequency of stimuli.

We are repeatedly faced with the problem of how to interpret the positive as well as the negative results. Several essentially similar tests on the same poisoned subject often give contradictory results with respect to impairment of the function of the nervous system (Horváth et al., 1961, 1963).

A low sensitivity to drugs has been repeatedly reported, especially when conditioned motor reflex techniques are used. One can devise experimental situations in which the poisoned animal performs the required conditioned activity until it loses consciousness. This has been observed in escape reactions (pedal pressing, shock avoidance) as well as in simple food rein-forcement experiments on rats exposed to high concentrations of trichloroethylene or large doses of narcotics. In the course of recovery the shock-avoidance and the food-approach responses reappear though the animals are still displaying total ataxia. The same has been found in long-term toxicity studies with carbon disulphide (Frantík, 1970).

Compensation is typical, especially for fixed natural activities immediately connected with an urgent drive and for cyclic automatic activities. By modifying the test procedures it is possible to increase substantially the response to drugs, for example by reducing the urgency of the situation. In our study, medium-intensity noise was substituted for electrical stimulation in an avoidance situation; the other experimental conditions remained the same. In another experiment the fixed cycles of so-called non-respondent alimentary activity were disrupted by the introduction of conditioned stimuli. The activity during the intervals between stimuli was more susceptible to spontaneous or drug-induced reduction, and the resulting oscillations in the activity level substantially affected the variability of the response to the stimuli. In the experiments with trichloroethylene, the artificial components inserted into the motor response recovered much more slowly from acute poisoning than did the simple conditioned food-approach response.

Results differ qualitatively and quantitatively from method to method, and also for the same procedure if different characteristics are recorded. Measuring only one component of spontaneous motor activity may lead to false results (Horváth *et al.*, 1961) and masking of abnormal pathological patterns of activity.

A similar dissociation was observed in conditioned reflexes, especially in operant responses. Presumably the failure of an operant response causes biologically unfavourable environmental

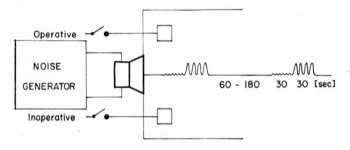

1	Percentage of stopped noise stimuli	EFFECTIVITY
2	Shortening of noise duration	SPEED
3	Number of pressing	SPECIFIC ACTIVITY
4	Motor differentiation	OPERANT COMPONENT
5	Stimulus control	RESPONDENT COMPONENT
6	Time decrement	DECREMENT
7	Duration of pressing	INERTNESS

FIG. 1. Essential features of the apparatus (above) and definition of the variable components of behaviour studied (below).

changes (e.g. electric shock) which tend—through the same feedback mechanisms as during training—to increase selectively the probability of some activities recurring and to decrease the probability of others. Selection pressure is directed against deviations in biologically effective characteristics, thus decreasing sensitivity to experimentally induced shifts in the nervous state.

The assumption that selection pressure makes it difficult to produce certain changes was tested in rats in an avoidance situation. A weak noise signal lasting 30 seconds followed immediately by a strong noise signal lasting 30 seconds was presented at one- to three-minute intervals. The pressing of one of two identical pedals stopped the sound stimulus until the start of the next noise period. By pressing the pedal permanently the noise could be avoided altogether (Fig. 1).

The first two variables in Table I determine the duration of the presence of the noxious agent. The effectiveness of the next three variables is less significant, and the last two, from the viewpoint of efficacy, are practically irrelevant. The variables subjected to intensive selection pressure had smaller spontaneous oscillations as well as lower inter-individual variability.

The effect of psychotropic drugs leads to the same conclusion. For example, the effects of amphetamine and caffeine on effectivity can hardly be proved, whereas the other items show an overall increase in activity at the expense of spatial and temporal differentiation, especially interference with the inert type of response. A similar pattern with a reversed trend of changes was observed after the administration of allobarbitone and chlorpromazine, and as a consequence of the long duration of the experiment.

An increase in the mean duration of lever pressing (increased inertness) was the only significant change in the avoidance response after exposure to concentrations of carbon disulphide or trichloroethylene which depress spontaneous motor activity by about 50 per cent, and the same was true of rats exposed to $2 \cdot 4$ mg/l carbon disulphide for three months.

Similarly, in human experiments using conditioned motor reflexes the prolonged pressing of the signal device—which was not explicitly included in the instruction—was the only characteristic by which workers who had been exposed to toxic substances for a long time differed from the control sample (Michalová and Horváth, 1956).

TABLE I

COMPARISON OF THE EFFECTS OF DIFFERENT DRUGS ON THE VARIABLE COMPONENTS OF AVOIDANCE RESPONSES IN RATS, AND A CORRELATION OF THESE VARIABLES WITH MOTOR ACTIVITY

Avoidance	Coefficient of variation	Amphet-amine 1–2 mg/kg	Caffeine 10–20 mg/kg	Allobarbi-tone 8 mg/kg	Chlorpro-mazine 1–2 mg/kg	Prolonged session	Correlation (linear) with motor activity		
							Intra-individual*	Inter-individual	
1 Effectivity	20	(↑)	~	→	(↓)	~	★		†
2 Speed	25	(↑)	~	→	(↓)	~	o	o	+
3 Activity	50	←	←	→	→	→	o	o	+
4 Operant	75	→	→	?	→	←	(+)	o	+
5 Respondent	66	←	?	→	→	~	o	o	+
6 Decrement	120	→ ↓	→ ↓	⇈	⇈	~				
7 Inert	77	⇈	⇈	⇈	⇈	⇈				
Actography									
Motor activity	42	⇈	⇈	↓↓	↓↓				

★ low { pedal position
† high { pedal position

The above experiments indicate that in suitable circumstances changes in the actual state or the phenotype manifest themselves in preference to a certain type of motor response (in our case, e.g., "inert") without any appreciable change in global "effectiveness". If one simple type of reaction is accentuated by the experimental technique, and alternatives are eliminated during the training period (e.g. by an instruction in human experiments), behavioural changes may not be apparent.

Distortion is also introduced by measuring characteristics of a stimulus-controlled activity. The resulting values cannot always be regarded as a representative of the actual functional state. As long as the presentation of stimuli depends on defined behavioural activities (which is frequently the case especially in animal experiments) the actual functional state at the moment of response is artificially standardized. This again leads to a reduction in spontaneous variability and in the sensitivity of response to experimental interventions.

To test this hypothesis, the spontaneous variability, drug-induced changes in reaction times, and other characteristics of alimentary motor responses were compared in rats in conditions in which the activity of the animal at the moment of signal presentation was standardized.

Analysis of the results showed that the spontaneous components of motor responses were more sensitive to drugs, and that normally well-correlated characteristics dissociated under the influence of psychotropic drugs (Table II). Medium doses of barbiturates slightly shortened the intervals between responses and the duration of the response. This may be interpreted as stimulatory action. In contrast, general activity was strongly depressed during the intervals between the responses, indicating that sedation and inhibition of competitive activities were responsible for the improved performance. On the other hand, medium doses of stimulants sometimes failed to shorten the re-action times and the intervals between the response. This was due to an increase in intersignal activity and the number of rapid but atypical responses. Moreover, the unreinforced atypical responses caused deterioration of subsequent conditioned responses.

Signal presentation, regardless of the activity of the animal, led to an increase in the reaction time and its variance. Simultaneously the drug effect changed substantially. Under conditions

TABLE II

DRUG INDUCED CHANGES IN SELECTED CHARACTERISTICS OF CONDITIONED
ALIMENTARY REACTIONS IN RATS

		Caffeine 5 mg/kg	Amphetamine		Allobarbitone	
			1 mg/kg	1·5 mg/kg	8 mg/kg	12 mg/kg
Intersignal activity		↑↑	↑	↑↑	↓	↓↓
Non-respondent						
Speed of	spontaneous component	↑↑	↑	↑↑	↑↓	↓↓
	response	↑↑	↓↑	↑	↑	↑
Respondent						
Number of reactions	optimal	↑↑	↓↑	↓↑	↑	↑↓
	atypical	↑	↑	↑	↓	↓
	abortive	↑	↑↑	↑↑	↓	↑
	delayed	↑	↓	↓	↓	↓
Non-reactions		↓	↑	↑	↓	↓

of standard activity at the moment of signal presentation, doses of barbiturate large enough to reduce general motor activity significantly shortened the reaction time and reduced the number of atypical responses. In conditions of an uncontrolled stimulus presentation, the effects on reaction time were reversed.

Control of the activity of the animal at the onset of the stimulus led to less variability in the actual functional state. But not even profound changes in the overall level of the functional state eliminated temporary normalization of behaviour. Therefore it is not surprising that if the signals are presented only during these short periods in which the animals have returned to the normal state, the typical effects of the drugs are not seen, except when relatively high doses are used.

These empiric arguments pertain to experimental chemical interventions in general, regardless of whether there are specifically differentiated effects of individual chemical agents or whether the models used cover the whole field of relevant neurotropic effects. If we reject purely speculative and anthropomorphic explanations we conclude that notwithstanding the mass of descriptive data on the different actions of different substances on different types of animal behavioural tests, enough information is not yet available to enable us to define a set of animal experimental procedures which would provide all the necessary information on the acute adverse effects on behaviour of most of the important new chemicals.

Tests on the acute deleterious effects of chemicals on human performance are in a more favourable position. Individual tests can be related—with varying exactness—to psychologically or physiologically defined types of higher nervous functions. Their relationship to the everyday activities of man is hence closer and can be more readily verified. But in some cases this is only seemingly so. For instance, one can hardly accept that a high correlation between the ability to perform a certain complex test and proficiency in a certain profession could be an argument for this test being suitable for predicting the effects of drugs on this specific type of professional activity. In complex performance tests (e.g. driving simulators) it is probable, if not certain, that the drug-affected psychological components will not be identical to those responsible for the ascertained correlation.

Neither will the attempt to imitate natural (e.g. occupational) conditions in the laboratory overcome the gap between the experimental results and their practical application. Some essential feature is always lacking in laboratory studies, especially the natural level of motivation and the negative factors related to the duration of the task. This lack must presumably influence the usefulness of all measures of performance, therefore it is not reliable to recommend that the results be applied practically.

Simple laboratory models allow a deeper analysis of chemically induced changes in performance. As there are many such studies it is surprising that only a few have been devoted to a systematic analysis of the factors of the human psychomotor performance that are specifically impaired by various groups of chemicals.

Mirski and Kornetsky (1964) have conducted a series of experiments in which the relatively low sensitivity of vigilance tests to barbiturates, and functionally related drugs, was compared with the sensitivity of cognitive tests. Chlorpromazine was found to have a reverse relationship which resembled the functional consequence of sleep deprivation. There were up to ten-fold differences in the sensitivity levels.

We compared the effects of drugs on performance in several tests which involved a different degree of vigilance, reaction alertness and cognition. The tests used were simple motor choice responses (a) to tachystoscopically presented visual patterns according to a learned code, (b) to short acoustic signals according to their localization, (c) to the detection of brief and slight change in flicker frequency. Various modifications of these basic tests were also used. A very simple and tiny motor response, a low intensity of stimuli and a monotonous background environment were included in the experimental design to make the sustaining of attention difficult. The findings in occupational medicine indicate that it is in just such conditions that the de-activating effects of, for example, sleep debt and probably chemical agents or internally caused distraction, are most dangerous.

Our tests revealed that performance was already impaired after the administration of relatively low doses of drugs (e.g. 250 mg hexobarbitone orally, 2 mg atropine subcutaneously, 5 mg benactyzine subcutaneously, 20 mg dl-amphetamine orally). The degree of impairment differed from one drug-test combination to the other; for example, 250 mg of hexobarbitone were needed to affect optical pattern discrimination, 375 mg to affect acoustic discrimination, and 500 mg to affect the detection of changes in flicker frequency. Amphetamine, in a dose which increased the rate of detection of changes in flicker frequency and shortened the reaction time, significantly impaired the ability of the same subjects to discriminate between acoustic stimuli.

The interaction of the effect of the drug with the duration of the test was another differentiating characteristic. Whereas the intensity of the hypnotic effects increased in the course of the serial task, the effect of drugs with predominantly autonomic actions (causing a secondary impairment of attention) was most marked in the beginning of the session.

The qualitative differences in acute (repeated) and chronic toxicity which frequently occur require different test procedures and criteria.

In our view the acute effects of slight poisoning reflect functional changes at the higher levels of organization, while deviations at lower levels (molecular, cellular) need not necessarily exceed the normal range. Thus acute changes may be related to the summation of small but synchronized shifts in many basic units. At this stage the first detectable deviations may be expected at higher levels of functional coordination.

In contrast, changes at a cellular level often predominate in chronic poisoning. Higher functional levels frequently show more or less complete compensation leading to negative findings in unspecific integral tests. On the other hand, the mental symptoms described in human chronic poisoning do not necessarily reflect an organic nervous lesion: chronicity may result from the interaction of repeated acute exposures to the chemical agent with repeated life stress. It may be justifiable to ask whether this is not the case in the majority of so-called chronic, chemically induced, behavioural disturbances.

In our experience the behavioural tests which have been used are neither satisfactory for studying these two separate aspects of chronic toxicity nor for answering these questions. Two possible ways seem to be promising: either to test the maximum acute functional load, or to use model situations in which the chronically poisoned animal would be exposed to repeated stressful situations.

The maximum motor capacity (maximum locomotor speed and endurance), measured on a treadmill with a programmed gradual increase in speed, proved to be a suitable measure of impairment in our studies on chronic carbon disulphide toxicity in rats. This technique allows assessment of the functional loss in the lower components of performance. Similar tests using acute stress on the higher nervous functions (e.g. reaction to intensive noise) or the cumulation of repeated stressful stimuli have not as yet produced unambiguous results.

Most experimental toxicological studies assess the potential hazards to man of long-term exposure to chemical agents on the basis of a single exposure or cumulative acute effects in animals. The general validity of the results of these studies is dubious. Probably the intensity of the direct chronic neurotropic action of some substances is proportional to the intensity of their acute effects, and the mechanism of action is similar. But for many substances the present knowledge indicates the opposite; for example, during chronic exposure of rats to carbon disulphide the acute symptoms, which resembled narcotic changes, disappeared and, after a behaviourally asymptomatic period, a progressive motor impairment appeared which could not be evoked either by massive acute exposure or by several subacute exposures. From this it follows that only a very preliminary idea on the intensity and character of direct neurotropic effects can be formulated on the basis of acute effects. The alternative is to seek for suitable specific tests.

QUANTITATIVE INTERPRETATION

There are problems in reliably interpreting the results of experiments designed to predict hazards. It is generally acknowledged that experimental biological data on the action of chemicals cannot be used directly for the quantitative prediction of hazard to man. Recognition of an effect does not establish the probability of a hazard. With the refinement of testing methods the criterion of noxious effect becomes difficult to lay down. The relationship of observed effects to physiological responses, adaptational reactions, compensatory processes or pathological changes becomes obscure. This applies to clinical diagnosis and even more to experimental research, especially to experiments on animals.

One way to validate test procedures indirectly is to apply them first to relatively well-investigated reference substances, as is done, for example, in pharmacological research. Comparison with a standard is commonly used for the prediction of specific effects of drugs. Less obvious is the suitability of such reference procedures for less specific effects of drugs and toxic substances.

We attempted to compare systematically the changes chemically induced in the behaviour of animals with the effects produced by standard reference substances, selected according to the type of reaction expected (Horváth et al., 1966).

The reference procedure involved three steps: (a) interpolation of equally effective concentrations from dose response curves; (b) coefficients of relative toxicity; (c) the combination of the coefficient of relative toxicity and the conventional threshold value for the corresponding reference substance to provide a partial estimate of the threshold value for the substance being studied (Table III).

The reliability of the whole complex of partial estimates depends (a) on the capacity of the complex of adopted techniques and functional characteristics to disclose all important aspects of toxic action and (b) on the choice of the reference substances (industrial chemicals or typical drugs) for the individual techniques.

This method of treating experimental toxicological data was originally proposed for the comparison of results in our own laboratory. Common reference substances would offer an opportunity for the comparison of results from different laboratories and for discussion of controversial results, thus facilitating the study of complex theoretical problems and contributing to the efforts to devise more valid criteria of hazard. A secondary, though no less important, result would be an objective comparison of various techniques and the gradual selection of the most efficient.

A similar procedure was applied to the testing of drug effects on the psychomotor capacity in man. As in animal toxicological experiments, the selection of appropriate reference substances for various types of effects is crucial if the comparison is to be valid. The appropriately selected reference substances may serve as a built-in standard for the comparison of various testing procedures (Hughes and Forney, 1964).

In man, in contrast to animal experiments, the doses which produce measurable effects are close to the critical level. Instead of the subjectively determined criterion of effect in animal tests, to which the effect of both the studied and the reference substance was related, it is possible to determine the criterion objectively by interpolating or extrapolating the dose equipotential to the critical dose of the reference substance.

Moreover, critical doses of reference drugs may be experimentally verified. This has been made possible primarily by the extensive statistical study of Borkenstein and co-workers (1964) on the relationship between the blood ethanol concentration of drivers and traffic accidents. It is impossible that a similar study could be performed for any other substance. But the known critical dose of ethanol might serve as a basis for the quantitative comparison of some drug effects. (A similar comparison in the form of so-called Alkohol-Äquivalent is used by Klein, Brüner and Wegmann, 1969.)

It is difficult to agree, however, to a direct comparison by means of laboratory tests because ethanol does not possess a series of effects which are substantial for the action of some drugs or *vice versa*, so that the ratio would not correspond in many cases to the ratio of hazard. It would be possible, however, to compare the effects of ethanol with the aid of a complex performance test approaching the demands of car driving, at least with representatives of the major drug groups, which would then serve as

7

TABLE III

AN EXAMPLE OF A REFERENCE PROCEDURE APPLIED TO EXPERIMENTAL EFFECTS OF FIVE SOLVENTS IN ANIMALS (UPPER PART), AND TWO DRUGS IN MAN (LOWER PART)

Test criteria	Reference substance and effective dose*	Carbon disulphide‡	Trichloro-ethylene‡	Benzene‡	Toluene‡	Xylene‡
(a)		**0·32**	**0·75**	**1·26**	**0·80**	**1·15**
Amphetamine sulphate	(1·8) 1·1	(5·6) 0·20	(2·4) 0·46	(1·4) 0·78	(2·2) 0·50	(1·6) 0·69
Caffeine and sodium benzoate	(19) 9·5	(59) 0·16	(25) 0·38¶	(15) 0·63¶	(24) 0·40¶	(17) 0·56¶
(b)		**0·64**	**2·80**	**6·30**	**>5·30**	**3·70**
Allobarbitone	(5·0) 4·8	(37) 0·13	(8·5) 0·56	(3·8) 1·3	(<4·5) >1·1	(6·5) 0·74
Chlorpromazine	(2·5) 1·6	(13) 0·11¶	(2·9) 0·48	(1·3) 1·1	(<1·5) >1·0	(2·2) 0·63

Test substance and effective concentration†

(c–g)		Atropine§ sulphate	Benactyzine§ hydrochloride
		0·04	**0·20**
(c)	Hexobarbitone (16) 23	(400) 0·06	
(d)	Hexobarbitone (23) 23	**0·04** (570) 0·04	
(e)	Hexobarbitone (31) 23	(780) 0·03¶	(155) 0·15¶
(f)	Hexobarbitone (31) 23		(155) 0·15
(g)	Hexobarbitone (23) 23		(155) 0·19

* μmol/kg, intraperitoneally in rats, orally in man.
† p.p.m. × 10³ or μmol/kg,
‡ Single dose subcutaneously, 10–120 minutes before testing.
§ Single 8–hour exposure just before measuring.
¶ Minimum estimates.

The figures in brackets are the coefficients of relative toxicity, i.e. the ratio of the effective concentration (dose) of the reference substance to the tested substance. The figures below and to the right of those in brackets are the partial estimates of human threshold concentration (in p.p.m. × 10³) or doses (in μmol/kg) for tested substances and for acute effect. The threshold dose of hexobarbitone is interpreted by Klein, Brunner and Wegmann (1969) as equipotential to 0·5% ethanol in the blood. The other threshold doses are chosen from medical practice. The experimentally determined human threshold concentration values are in bold print.

Test criteria: a: increase in spontaneous motor activity (SMA) in rats by 30%; *b*: depression of SMA by 50%; *c*: tachystoscopic pattern discrimination (TPD) in man—reaction time lengthened by 10%; *d*: number of TPD errors increased by 10%; *e*: acoustical discrimination in man (AD)—reaction time lengthened by 10%; *f*: number of AD errors increased by 5%; *g*: visual vigilance in man—stimulus threshold increased by 0·8 c.p.s.

reference drugs for individual types of effects. Thus one of the objectives outlined by Goldberg and Havard (1968) in the cited research programme would be achieved.

As we know of no such study we have used in the example given in Table III, the results of Klein, Brüner and Wegmann (1969), even though the method used by them probably does not guarantee the general validity of the ratio obtained.

SUMMARY

Testing methods using higher nervous functions have a long-standing tradition in screening and in the quantitative assessment of the effects of chemical substances. Nonetheless in a number of cases the suitability of their application is questionable.

On the basis of our own findings we point out some possible reasons for their failure, due primarily to the more or less random choice of techniques, the adoption of methods and functional indicators from other disciplines without regard for the specificity of chemical action, and the artificial standardization of indicators.

A reference procedure is demonstrated for the "translation" of the quantitative laboratory results into a practically applicable profile of toxicity.

REFERENCES

BARNES, J. M., and DENZ, F. A. (1954). *Pharmac. Rev.*, **6**, 191–242.
BORKENSTEIN, R. E., GROWTHER, R. F., SHUMATE, R. F., ZIEL, W. B., and
    ZYLMAN, R. (1964). *The Role of the Drinking Driver in Traffic Accidents*,
    ed. Dale, A. Bloomington: Department of Police Administration,
    Indiana University.
FRANTÍK, E. (1970). *Medicine del Lavoro*. In press.
GOLDBERG, L., and HAVARD, J. D. J. (1968). *Research on the Effects of Alcohol
    and Drugs on Driver Behaviour and their Importance as a Cause of Road
    Accidents*. Paris: OECD.
HORVÁTH, M. (1961). *Pure appl. Chem.*, **3**, 171–174.
HORVÁTH, M., and FORMÁNEK, J. (1954). *Pracovní Lék.*, **6**, 336–346.
HORVÁTH, M., FRANTÍK, E., FORMÁNEK, J., and MIKISKA, A. (1961). In
    Proc. XIII Int. Congr. occup. Health, New York, 1960, pp. 714–721.
HORVÁTH, M., FRANTÍK, E., GROSMANOVÁ, E., and MIKISKOVÁ, H. (1966).
    In *Proc. XV Congr. Int. Medecine du Travail*, suppl. III, p. 97. Wien:
    Wiener Medizinische Akademie. [(1967). *Pracovní Lék.*, **19**, 433–440.]

HORVÁTH, M., FRANTÍK, E., KOŘÍNEK, F., MIKISKA, A., and MIKISKA, H. (1963). In *IIème Symposium International sur les limites Tolérables pour les Substances Toxiques dans l'Industrie* (Proceedings of IUPAC International Symposium, Paris), ed. Truhaut, R. Paris: Institut National de Sécurité.

HUGHES, F. W., and FORNEY, R. B. (1964). *Clin. Pharmac. Ther.*, **5,** 414–421.

KLEIN, K. E., BRÜNER, H., and WEGMANN, H. M. (1969). *Wehrmed. Mschr.*, **13,** 193–199.

MICHALOVÁ, C., and HORVÁTH, M. (1956). *Čas. lék. česk.*, **95,** 1160–1167.

MIRSKI, A. F., and KORNETSKY, C. (1964). *Psychopharmacologia*, **5,** 161–177.

SMYTH, H. F., JR. (1956). *Am. ind. Hyg. Ass. Q.*, **17,** 129–185.

TRUHAUT, R. (1964). *Archs envir. Hlth*, **8,** 487–491.

WHO (1965). *Psychoactive Drugs and Road Safety*, No. WHO/PT/128.

WHO (1968). *Human Factors in Road Accidents* (EURO 0147). Copenhagen: WHO Regional Office for Europe. [See, (1964). *WHO Chron.*, **23,** 205–211.]

WHO (1969). *Tech. Rep. Ser. Wld Hlth Org.*, No. 415.

OCCUPATIONAL HAZARDS AND BEHAVIOUR STUDIES

J. M. Barnes

MRC Toxicology Unit, Carshalton, Surrey

Occupational hazards may often result from chemical influences. "Mad as a hatter" describes the symptoms of poisoning by mercury, which is used in felting wool, and mercury vapour can undoubtedly affect behaviour. A study of people occupationally exposed to a particular chemical might therefore be the best point at which to start investigating a substance believed to affect the general population.

Occupational exposure to a toxic chemical may threaten health by causing a specific toxic syndrome, such as lead encephalopathy. Tiller, Schilling and Morris (1968) found a high incidence of ischaemic heart disease in a group of people occupationally exposed to what had hitherto been considered safe levels of carbon disulphide. This suggests that exposure to some chemicals may lead to an increased incidence of a "natural disease". I do not know whether occupational exposure to toxic chemicals can cause an increased susceptibility to psychopathic disorders, although toxic doses of carbon disulphide do induce acute mania.

In trying to assess the existence of such hazards it is necessary to be able to measure accurately the toxic levels to which individuals are exposed. Random monitoring of the atmosphere is rarely enough to indicate the true differences in the exposures of individuals to a toxic chemical because the atmospheric concentrations of the chemical may vary between adjacent sites; resort must be made to measurements of metabolites in the blood and excreta, or occasionally to the levels stored in the tissues. I doubt where individual differences in susceptibility have been seriously considered, with the exception of hypersensitivity, when assessing the incidence of occupational poisoning. Differences in response are usually assumed to reflect differences in exposure.

The question raised in this study group is whether behavioural tests provide a useful guide to likely hazards. As there is much doubt about the relevance of animal behavioural studies to man, I am surprised that more work is not being done with alcohol, especially when there is so much information about its effects on human performance, for example on car driving (Drew, Colquhoun and Long, 1959). Rats could be trained to perform equivalent tasks and the changes induced by alcohol studied. If the pattern of change was similar to that in humans, this might give some encouragement to the idea that animals respond in a similar way to man, at least in certain types of tests.

In the post-war years there was increasing interest in the so-called safe or acceptable threshold limit values for toxic substances in various occupational environments. It soon became obvious that there were striking differences between the permissible atmospheric levels recommended in the USSR and Eastern Europe, and those in the USA and Western Europe. Much of the data from the USSR seemed to be derived from the effects of toxic substances on conditioned reflexes. When such reflexes are established in normal people the responses can be detected from changes in EEG patterns. However, once a conditioned reflex is established to the smell of a substance such as sulphur dioxide, a response can be elicited at levels below those that can be consciously detected and below those normally considered hazardous. As sulphur dioxide never reaches the brain, obviously it is the response of the olfactory end-organs to the sulphur dioxide molecules that is being detected. This illustrates the crucial point in all these behavioural tests: if a toxic substance elicits a response, behavioural or biochemical, does this mean that it is hazardous to the organism?

A recent WHO report (1969) indicated that international agreement on threshold limit values for a number of very different compounds has now been reached. The figure given for sulphur dioxide, for example, suggests that the conditioned reflex response is no longer regarded by the USSR as a criterion of toxicity.

Our experience has suggested that effects on behaviour are not necessarily a sensitive index of response to a toxic substance. Russell, Watson and Frankenhauser (1961) investigated the effects of anticholinesterases and obtained significant behavioural effects only when the level of brain cholinesterase was depressed by 50 per cent or more. However, reduction in blood cholinesterase activity can be detected biochemically before this level is reached.

For many years we have been interested in trialkyl tin compounds which specifically inhibit oxidative phosphorylation in the brain. In rats dosed with triethyl tin, biochemical changes could be detected before behavioural changes (M. Khairy, unpublished). The same applied to rats poisoned with methyl mercury salts, which eventually produce specific neuronal damage. Even if behavioural changes are not necessarily a very sensitive index of toxicity this does not mean that behavioural tests should never be carried out. However, the effects of a compound on the central nervous system are not necessarily its most important toxic effects. Benzene, toluene and xylene may be ranked according to their effects as narcotics, but it is benzene, not toluene or xylene, that damages the bone marrow, and it is this effect that determines the acceptable level of exposure. In toxicological investigations, therefore, behavioural tests should be related to the other biological effects caused by the substances being studied.

Behaviour tests with rats may lead to unexpected findings which are unrelated to behaviour. With 200 p.p.m. DDT in their diet the gait angle of rats was normal, but it increased progressively in rats on a diet containing 300 p.p.m. and 400 p.p.m. DDT. However, the rats on 100 p.p.m. had a gait angle that was less than normal (Khairy, 1959). These differences in gait pattern almost certainly reflect a physiological disturbance such as that involving sodium efflux from nerve endings under the influence of DDT as suggested by Narahashi and Haas (1968).

Behaviour tests inevitably involve a close study of the experimental animals, and this may be sadly lacking in some procedures commonly used in testing for safety.

Behavioural studies may add mystery to already complex situations. Labelle, Zinger and Bevilacqua (1963) reported striking changes in the learning ability of rats exposed to laboratory air containing positively or negatively charged ions. There is a great deal of controversy as to whether the electrical state of the air affects people's feeling of well-being and hence presumably their behaviour. Concern has been expressed about the possible effects of changes in the electrical state of the air in closed environments, such as submarines, space vehicles and even air-conditioned buildings. It would be interesting to know whether people respond like Labelles's rats, by alterations in their rates of learning under such conditions.

My conclusion is that while simple behaviour tests may be useful as screening methods when looking for active compounds, they form only a small part of a general study when one is trying to understand toxic mechanisms and define toxic hazards.

REFERENCES

Drew, G. C., Colquhoun, W. P., and Long, H. A. (1959). *MRC Memorandum*, No. 38. London: HMSO.

Khairy, M. (1959). *Q. Jl exp. Psychol.*, **11**, 84–91.

Labelle, C. W., Zinger, B. L., Bevilacqua, D. M. (1963). In *IIème Symposium International sur les Limites Tolérables pour les Substances Toxiques dans l'Industrie* (Proceedings of IUPAC International Symposium, Paris), pp. 171–180, ed. Truhaut, R. Paris: Institut National de Sécurité.

Narahashi, T., and Haas, H. G. (1968). *J. gen. Physiol.*, **51**, 177.

Russell, R. W., Watson, R. H. J., and Frankenhauser, M. (1961). *Scand. J. Psychol.*, **2**, 21.

Tiller, J. R., Schilling, R. S. F., and Morris, J. N. (1968). *Br. med. J.*, **4**, 407–411.

WHO. (1969). *Tech. Rep. Ser. Wld Hlth Org.*, No. 415.

DISCUSSION

Boyland: Behavioural changes are only one aspect of toxicity, but it should be possible to obtain results about toxicity more quickly than when testing for carcinogenic action.

The use of lead tetraethyl in petrol is an economy measure. Is it difficult to say whether the amount of lead in the air of cities is harmful?

Barnes: We should look at the other toxins produced by gasoline fumes, nitrous oxides and reaction products with ozone, for example.

Sandler: Krueger and his colleagues have made extensive observations on the effect of ionized air on biological systems. They found that it will deplete tissues of 5-hydroxytryptamine

(Krueger, Andriese and Kotaka, 1968; Krueger and Kotaka, 1969). These findings are to some extent complemented by the observations of Sulman (1969) that the khamsin, a wind sweeping in from the desert in the Middle East and containing a relatively high content of ionized air, causes an increased urinary output of the major metabolite of 5-hydroxytryptamine, that is 5-hydroxyindoleacetic acid.

Barnes: Krueger has studied the effect of ions on tracheal cilia, but people are reluctant to accept his results. A problem in research on ions is that the physicists who know something about ions are not able to assess biological effects, and the biologists often know little about the ions they believe they are generating. I have asked visitors from Israel about their reactions to the khamsin and find very striking differences in their replies: some feel better, some feel worse, and some can't tell the difference and are very critical about those who can.

Steinberg: Small doses of alcohol and also barbiturates are known to increase activity and certain kinds of performance in animals, whereas in large doses these compounds have the opposite effect (Kinnard and Carr, 1957; Rushton and Steinberg, 1963; Barry, 1968).

Barnes: Is the correlation between these effects in animals and man good?

Steinberg: It is difficult to answer this simply, since the behaviour measured in animals and in man in these experiments is usually different. For example, in man small doses of alcohol have been found to counteract the adverse effects of sleep-deprivation on complex reaction times (Wilkinson and Colquhoun, 1968). An analogous experiment could be set up with laboratory animals, using appropriate discrimination tasks, but it would be quite tricky to get comparable conditions and I do not know whether it has been tried.

Brimblecombe: The rat seems to be curiously resistant to the effects of alcohol and so predictions of effective doses in man on the basis of rat experiments would be quite wrong.

Some work with alcohol has been done with cats. The animals were conditioned to press a lever and then a blast of air was blown at them. They developed a "neurosis", and when they were then given the choice of drinking milk or alcohol, they chose to drink alcohol.

Silverman: Miller, who has studied alcohol extensively, found that it reduced what he called fear (Miller and Barry, 1960).

Steinberg: The rat will voluntarily drink solutions containing up to about 8 per cent alcohol in preference to ordinary water (Richter, 1957; Veale and Myers, 1969).

Beckett: Was the level of alcohol in the blood correlated with effect, or are you just talking about the dose given?

Brimblecombe: In our experiments we did not measure blood-levels. I am talking about the dose given, which on the basis of dosage in man would have been enormous. It may be due to the differences in metabolism of alcohol in the rat and in man.

Steinberg: To show up behavioural effects rodents usually have to be given larger doses weight for weight than man.

Brimblecombe: This is not consistently so. We have looked at many psychotropic drugs in the open-field situation, and the ratio between the minimal effective dose in the rat and the generally accepted minimal effective dose in man varies between 1 and about 1000. Our results are absolutely valueless for predicting dose, but they may be useful to predict a type of effect in man.

Steinberg: The absolute doses cannot be predicted but the shape of the dose response curve is often consistent. For example, chlordiazepoxide (Librium) can be shown to be active over a much wider range of doses in experiments on the spontaneous activities of rats than amylobarbitone. With amylobarbitone the range of doses between the dose which produced just discernible stimulant effects and that which produced sedation to the point of inactivity was $3 \cdot 75$ to $60 \cdot 0$ mg/kg; with chlordiazepoxide just discernible stimulant effects were obtained with $1 \cdot 56$ mg/kg, but even with 400 mg/kg some activity was still present (Rushton and Steinberg, 1963; see also Steinberg and Tomkiewicz, this volume, p. 201 *et seq.*).

King: Dr Barnes, are behavioural tests in relation to what you are interested in rather insensitive?

Barnes: Yes.

King: If one does not do parametric investigations, for example, varying the activity level or the difficulty of the problem, one is unlikely to pick up significant effects. Ideally, one would always work at a threshold level where there is just sufficient stimulus to control the behaviour. This is the area where behaviour becomes maximally sensitive to modification by a drug. I suspect that toxicological investigations are usually done under constant environmental conditions. There is a dichotomy here between the need for stability of behaviour for the purposes of observation and the sensitivity of behaviour to chemical treatment. Drug studies in which parametric investigations have not been done can be misleading because one can conclude more or less anything one likes by choosing arbitrary values. Behavioural studies in toxicology must be far more comprehensive before one can conclude that they do not add very much to the information already available from pharmacological studies.

Barnes: But you concluded you presentation by saying that with the tests you used you could not tell the difference between chlorpromazine and a barbiturate. Are these the types of tests that you would have expected to be sensitive to differences in behaviour?

King: This conclusion, drawn from the tests which I was doing to investigate these two compounds, is true if you ignore the distinctions between these two drugs, which pharmacologically have many similar features. One of the main results of our conditioned avoidance studies was that the effect of both these drugs was related to the intensity of the shock that controlled the behaviour, and that this relationship was multiplicative not additive. If one only works at the upper limits of the intensity range there will be no observable effects.

Weiskrantz: Several questions are intertwined here. If by toxicity one means the occurrence of pathological changes in the tissues eventually leading to death, then it is doubtful if behavioural tests on animals can be predictive and useful. But where one is interested in possible behavioural disturbances in man then logically one is compelled to analyse behaviour in animals. It may sometimes be easier to pick up biochemical effects than to measure behaviour, but the biochemical effects must eventually be related to behaviour. There can be no detour. Whether any particular study in animals will usefully predict behaviour in man is usually an empiric matter which cannot be decided in advance.

Barnes: Much of the work on assessing toxic substances is concerned with finding the margin of safety; we want to know if a dose that does not produce an obvious pathological effect in animals is a non-effective dose. It is in an attempt to solve this sort of problem that it has been suggested that effects on the CNS would be a more sensitive index of toxicity than the tests that are currently available.

REFERENCES

BARRY, H. (1968). *J. comp. physiol. Psychol.*, **65**, 349.

KINNARD, W. J., and CARR, K. J. (1957). *J. Pharm. Pharmac.*, **121**, 354.

KRUEGER, A. P., ANDRIESE, P. C., and KOTAKA, S. (1968). *Int. J. Biometeorol.*, **12**, 225.

KRUEGER, A. P., and KOTAKA, S. (1969). *Int. J. Biometeorol.*, **13**, 25.

MILLER, N. E., and BARRY, H. (1960). *Psychopharmacologia*, **1**, 169–199.

RICHTER, C. P. (1957). In *Neuropharmacology*, p. 39, ed. Abramson, H. A. New York: Macy.

RUSHTON, R., and STEINBERG, H. (1963). *Br. J. Pharmac. Chemother.*, **21**, 295.

SULMAN, F. G. (1969). *Abstr. IV Int. Pharmac. Congr.* Basel, p. 395.

VEALE, W. L., and MYERS, R. (1969). *Psychopharmacologia*, **15**, 361.

WILKINSON, R. T., and COLQUHOUN, W. P. (1968). *J. exp. Psychol.*, **76**, 623.

GENERAL DISCUSSION

Brimblecombe: Professor Weiskrantz is right to emphasize that when one is dealing with substances which are suspected of being able to influence behaviour, then behavioural studies must be done in animals at some stage. Such studies are, however, often clumsy, difficult to interpret, and not necessarily relevant, and if it is possible subsequently to substitute some simpler testing procedures, this should be done.

King: Behavioural tests are not clumsy! Although, of course, if one is only prepared to measure one aspect of an animal's behaviour, then they are clumsy because no worthwhile information is likely to be forthcoming.

Weiskrantz: The advantage of looking for any particular biochemical indicant, monoamine oxidase for example, is that the indicant is only valid if the particular biochemical indicant can be directly linked to the behaviour in question. In the case of monoamine oxidase inhibition, an antidepressant action must be shown. The fact that the relationship between chemical and behavioural effects is not well established is one of the reasons progress in the development of the antidepressants is slow.

Silverman: The toxicologists and the psychologists are at cross-purposes here. Dr Brimblecombe is advocating behavioural tests as screening processes, whereas Dr King would like precise effects of drugs on behaviour to be defined. In biochemical assessments, a specific test can be devised to answer a specific question; for example an enzyme can be isolated and its formula thus determined. Although we cannot yet do the equivalent of this in our behavioural tests, we should distinguish between the concepts of behavioural tests as wide-spectrum screening tests, and as tests of specific hypotheses.

Spinks: I agree; we are trying to be too subtle. If one tests drugs known to affect the CNS in man by the sorts of techniques one would use to assess the toxicity of a known liver poison, there is usually no doubt about their effect on the CNS. Much of our discussions have been centred round the possibility that drugs which in animals show little effect by our crude tests, could be shown to be potentially toxic in man through the use of more subtle animal tests. But we have not yet found an example of this; all the compounds that have been mentioned as having subtle behavioural effects in man, in much larger doses have very obvious effects on the CNS in animals.

Paget: Smoking is an example of a drug with unpredictable effects in man. We know that, socially, smoking is associated with detectable behavioural patterns, but whether these are due to nicotine or to some other component of the social smoking act which is associated with the use of tobacco we do not know; and the same is true of cannabis. These subtle alterations in behaviour are not predictable from any behavioural studies I have heard of.

Weiskrantz: Is there any way you could predict these patterns?

Paget: I do not know of any. This is the sort of question which it is legitimate for society to ask and which we try to answer for many drugs. Suppose that a pharmaceutical company wants to produce a new chemical on a vast scale. We have to decide if its manufacture will be safe for the operators or if they will develop, say, bladder cancer. Perhaps we should also ask if they are likely to go home and beat their wives.

Philp: It is, of course, important to decide why one uses a test before using it. And the critical appraisal by other workers of any such test depends on the way it is defined. Dr Barnes' statement that in some tests the investigator had obviously never observed the animal from the moment it was put into the cage to the moment it appeared on the post-mortem table is important. As scientists in the pharmaceutical industry we spend much of our time trying to make sure that the materials we handle are not harmful to, say, the rat or the mouse and, therefore, are probably not harmful to man. We look at the biological functions of these animals during life, study their bodily secretions and biochemistry, and we conclude our tests with a thorough pathological examination. But we seldom take the trouble to find out if their general pattern of activity has been altered by the drug under test; whether this has made them somnolent or aggressive or irritable and so on. During the past six years we have devised a battery of fairly simple tests to study these sorts of animal activity. We are, of course, using animals which we believe, from straightforward analysis, to be biologically normal. Although our results with these new tests are often negative, we think that we have added another dimension to our observations on animals and that this is entirely different from the more usual behavioural studies.

Weiskrantz: Unfortunately, if one is interested in possible adverse effects, one cannot do every possible test; we cannot prove the universal negative. But in some cases it is impossible to pick up a defect without the use of a subtle behavioural test. For example, an animal with a lesion in the neocortex in the temporal lobe looks normal and appears to be normal on even the more subtle behavioural tests. Nevertheless, these animals have severe and persistent difficulty in visual discrimination learning The best way, short of post-mortem examination, of picking out the animals with this sort of damage would be by appropriate behavioural tests, such as the ones you are using.

Paget: The difficulty we are having in communicating between the two sides of this question of the value of behaviour tests reflects the genuine difficulty of the problem. An issue that is currently being debated is the advisability or otherwise of making cannabis freely available for smoking. Toxicologically cannabis seems to be a rather innocuous drug, but to demonstrate merely that it has an effect on the CNS is irrelevant. What we need to know is this: in what circumstances is the use of cannabis likely to give rise to behavioural toxicity ?

Cowley: Part of the problem lies in defining behaviour. Hinde (1966) has suggested that behaviour can be described in two ways: first, in terms of the simple motor reflex movements (the strength, degree and patterning of muscular contractions) and second, in terms of some end product or consequence, such as drinking or smoking. The problem with cannabis, or any toxic agent, is to identify not only the immediate motor changes but also the long-term effects that society is interested in. The physiologist has tended to focus his attention on the former—the student of behaviour on the latter.

King: Cannabis is an excellent illustration of this problem. The work of Weil, Zinberg and Nelsen (1968) and Weil and Zinberg (1969) demonstrated how difficult it is to uncover these subtle effects. In their first paper (1968) on the effects of cannabis on naive subjects, almost no behavioural changes were shown, but in a later paper (1969), in which speech patterns of subjects under the influence of cannabis were analysed, behavioural

changes were detected; however, these effects were extremely
subtle and difficult to find.

Paget: If cannabis were a new form of sweetening agent, then
every toxicological laboratory in the world would be feeding
it to rats, mice and dogs, in order to find out if the drug were a
carcinogen. But, as far as I know, none of the committees that
have considered cannabis have seriously suggested that it should
be remitted to the laboratory for study. The situation for cannabis
resembles a decision to pass a sweetening agent for general
consumption on the basis of the opinion of a flavour-testing
panel.

Boyland: My impression is that effects of cannabis on speech are
permanent. The subjects have a new language with very few
words.

King: The pauses between words, not the speech itself, are said
to be the most sensitive indicator of chronic cannabis intoxi-
cation.

Steinberg: Pauses between words have been shown to be sensitive to such drugs as chlorpromazine (Goldman-Eisler, 1968).

ANIMAL BEHAVIOUR MODELS IN PSYCHOPHARMACOLOGY

Steinberg*: Much of this discussion has been about predicting
the psychological effects of drugs and of other chemicals on man
from the results of experiments on animal behaviour. Doubt has
been cast on the value and indeed the possibility of making such
extrapolations at all, and I should therefore like to define them.

A basic procedure is, first, to define the human behaviour
which one wishes to modify by drugs; second, to try to mimic
crucial aspects of this behaviour in animals; third, to test which
drugs, in which doses and precise circumstances, can alter this
animal behaviour; and finally and most important, to return to
the human behaviour and see whether the conclusions drawn from
the animal experiments are valid (Russell, 1960: Steinberg, 1961).

I disagree with Dr Brimblecombe that one should get away
from behavioural testing as soon as possible. In the present state
of our knowledge there is no certain way of predicting behavioural
effects from, for example, the pharmacological or biochemical
properties of drugs, and if there is a discrepancy between what

* In collaboration with Michal Tomkiewicz

8*

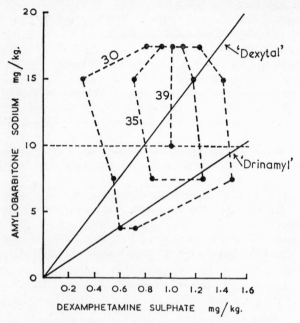

FIG. I. (*Steinberg*). Isobol diagram showing dose combinations which produced equal effects on the activity of rats
in a Y-maze. The outer contour was plotted by joining
points representing those dose combinations under the
influence of which the animals made 30 entries into the
arms of the maze. The inner contour represents 35 entries,
and the central vertical line joins two dose combinations
which yielded 39 entries, i.e. very high activity. No
ataxia was detected with mixtures which contained 10 mg/kg
amylobarbitone or less, and a line has been drawn at this level.
The lines radiating from the origin indicate two constant
ratios of dexamphetamine to amylobarbitone. These ratios
correspond to those in "Drinamyl" (1:6.5) and "Dexytal"
(1:13).

For each of these two ratios shown there is a range of doses
which produces high activity (35 entries or more) in rats, but
only with the "Drinamyl" ratio can high activity be produced without ataxia (After Rushton and Steinberg, 1967).

ought to happen on the basis of such properties and the behavioural effects which are observed when the drug is given to man, then by definition it is the behavioural effects, and the test methods used to establish them, which are right.

I should like to suggest that one example of such a reciprocal extrapolation between animals and man is contained in our work (Rushton and Steinberg, 1963, 1967) on amphetamine-barbiturate combinations. In most respects these two types of drug have predominantly opposite actions on the brain. In our experiments, moderate doses of either drug on its own had little effect on the spontaneous activity of rats in a novel environment. But when the two drugs were combined and given as mixtures, the activity of the rats was dramatically increased. Moreover, in these mixtures the ratios of the two drugs which were most effective in increasing the rats' activity were almost the same as the ratios in the two commercial amphetamine-barbiturate mixtures (Drinamyl and Dexytal) which have been most widely used for treating mild anxiety and depression (Fig. 1). The ratios in these clinically used products seem to have been arrived at empirically, without a pharmacological basis. Analagous amphetamine-barbiturate combinations have also been found to produce a "better" mood than the separate constituent drugs in normal volunteers (Dickins, Lader and Steinberg, 1965).

We have also carried out experiments with dexamphetamine mixed with chlordiazepoxide (Librium), a drug which is now widely used for similar purposes as small doses of barbiturates, although it is chemically and, in many respects, pharmacologically different. The behavioural measure, as with the amphetamine-barbiturate combinations, was the number of times a naive rat spontaneously entered the arms of a symmetrical Y-shaped runway in five minutes; this measure mainly depends on the amount of walking that the rat does. Again, neither drug on its own had a significant effect, but with several doses of the mixture there was a large increase in activity (Rushton and Steinberg, 1966), which was, again, much greater than the sum of the effects of any dose of the ingredients given separately (Fig. 2). The peak performance with the chlordiazepoxide-dexamphetamine mixture was marginally higher than the maximum obtainable with amylobarbitone-amphetamine mixtures. Further, chlordiazepoxide in combination with dexamphetamine was active over a

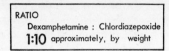

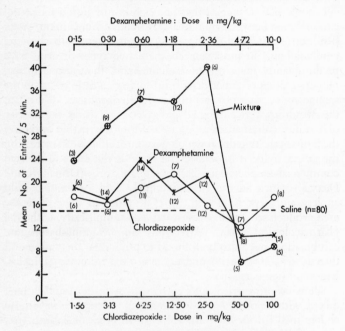

FIG. 2 (*Steinberg*). Activity of *rats* given dexamphetamine and chlordiazepoxide separately and in combination over a range of doses. The ordinate shows the number of entries into the arms of a Y-shaped runway during a 5 min trial. Each point represents mean results for a different group of rats; the number of animals in each group is given in brackets. The ratio of the two drugs was kept constant at approximately 1:10 by weight. The peak mixture effect is much greater than any of the effects of either of the separate drugs (results obtained by Rushton and Steinberg).

much wider range of doses by weight (approximately threefold) than was amylobarbitone; this is consistent with the greater clinical safety of chlordiazepoxide. Even with the highest doses of the dexamphetamine-chlordiazepoxide mixture the animals, though sluggish and ataxic, were still able to move about the maze.

On the basis of these animal results we tested a mixture of 5 mg dexamphetamine plus 20 mg chlordiazepoxide in human subjects (Besser and Steinberg, 1967). It increased the number of "desirable" feelings and sensations reported, and also significantly improved performance in a digit symbol substitution test (Wechsler, 1955); this again illustrates a parallel between effects in the rat and man, but it seems unlikely that amphetamine-chlordiazepoxide mixtures will be widely tried clinically since amphetamine is at present regarded with suspicion as liable to lead to addiction.

Recently we have studied whether the striking effects of the dexamphetamine-chlordiazepoxide mixtures in the rat and man can be reproduced in another species (mice) and in a different test situation (a holeboard) (Dorr et al., 1970). This has already been demonstrated for amphetamine-barbiturate combinations (Joyce et al., 1968; Bradley et al., 1968). We also wondered if the abnormally high activity produced by the mixtures would still be present if the animals were again exposed to a similar experimental situation, but this time without drugs. Previous work (Stern, 1960; Ross and Schnitzer, 1963; Rushton, Steinberg and Tinson, 1963; Rushton, Steinberg and Tomkiewicz, 1968; Cochin and Kornetsky 1964; Bohdanecky and Jarvik, 1967; Sachs, 1967; Kornetsky and Bain, 1968; Overton, 1968) had shown that various after-effects, which can be long-lasting, may occur in animals even after a single drug administration. (For examples of after-effects in man, see Joyce, 1970).

Naive male mice, Porton strain, were tested on a board with 16 symmetrically spaced holes (Boissier and Simon, 1962). Each mouse was placed singly on the board for three minutes and the number of times it dipped its head into the holes was counted. This, like walking in the Y-maze, may be regarded as a test of spontaneous exploratory activity. Like the Y-maze test, the holeboard also involves walking and this was scored in addition to the head dipping. The mice were given dex-amphetamine or chlordiazepoxide or a mixture of these two drugs intraperitoneally in a 1:10 ratio, 20 minutes before being placed on the board. The resulting dose-response curves (Fig. 3) strikingly resembled those obtained with rats tested in the Y-maze

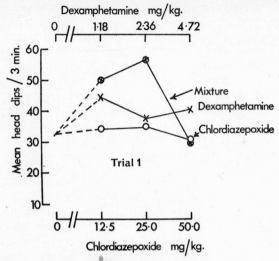

FIG. 3 (*Steinberg*). Activity of *mice* under the influence of dexamphetamine or chlordiazepoxide given alone and in combination in a constant ratio of approximately 1:10 by weight. The mice were tested on a hole-board, and the number of times they dipped their heads into the holes during a 3-min trial is shown on the ordinate. Each point represents the mean for 8 mice, and there were 24 controls. The peak mixture effect occurs at the same doses as in rats (Fig. 2), and is, as with rats, much greater than the highest activity obtainable with any dose of the separate drugs. (Results obtained by Dorr, Joyce, Porsolt, Steinberg, Summerfield and Tomkiewicz.)

Again, the drugs given separately hardly altered activity, but with the mixture there was a highly significant increase in the number of head dips [Kruskal-Wallis one-way analysis of variance, $H = 15.440$, $d.f. = 3$, $P < 0.01$ (Siegel, 1956)]; the curve showed the characteristic inverted "U" shape. The absolute doses of the mixture effective in rats and in mice were also closely similar.

When the same mice were retested one week later without any drugs or injections (trial II), the absolute amounts of activity fell by approximately 50 per cent, but the shapes of the dose-response curves obtained from the drug trials (trial I) re-emerged ($P < 0.001$). Fig. 4 shows the results only for the mixtures, though

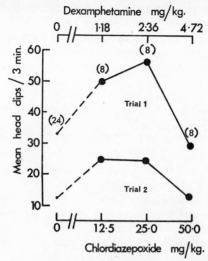

FIG. 4 (*Steinberg*). Mean number of head dips in 3 min by mice given a mixture of dexamphetamine and chlordiazepoxide at trial I (cf. Fig. 3). At trial II the same animals were tested on the same apparatus, but without any drugs or injections. The absolute amount of activity in each group was reduced by approximately 50% but the shape of the dose-response curve re-emerged at trial II. (Results obtained by Dorr, Joyce, Porsolt, Steinberg, Summerfield and Tomkiewicz.)

the curves for animals given the drugs separately were also very similar to those obtained at trial I, but again 50 per cent lower. When the amounts of walking on the board as distinct from the number of head dips were examined, substantially similar results both at trial I and trial II, were found.

These results show that the amount of activity at the second, drugless, trial was reduced by a constant proportion, regardless of the drugs or the doses administered at trial I. This decrease was presumably due to habituation, that is, the environment was now less novel and elicited less exploratory activity (cf. Rushton, Steinberg and Tinson, 1963).

The re-emergence of dose-response curves without any drugs may seem surprising. It is unlikely that the drugs or their active metabolites could still have been present in the bodies of the mice after one week (Koechlin *et al.*, 1965; Placidi and Cassano, 1968; Van der Kleijn, 1969).

The most reasonable explanation for our findings seems to be that the original drug experience had been "remembered", and that re-exposure of the mice to the environment in which it had occurred evoked their previous behaviour. Gross observations of how the animals moved about at trial II also suggested that they were in some sense trying to re-enact their original behaviour—though at trial II they appeared more hesitant, sniffed more and walked less deliberately than they did at trial I.

Shepherd, Lader and Rodnight (1968) have defined placebo effects in man as "those elements in drug effects which cannot be ascribed to pharmacodynamic action". Placebo effects are the result of complex interactions between the patients, the drug and the social and physical setting in which the drug is administered; each of these can modify the effects of the others. The therapeutic setting, for example, can modify the effectiveness of a particular drug and the drug itself can in turn either accentuate or attenuate the effects of the environment.

We suggest that the results just described might be regarded as an animal analogue of a "drug-induced placebo effect" and are yet another example of how animal and human psychopharmacology can mutually reinforce each other.*

Beckett: You claim that the rats showed increased behavioural effects with the amphetamine-barbiturate combinations. What test did you use in man as a basis for this correlation?

Steinberg: We used ordinary laboratory tests, for example, "digit-symbol substitution" speed of copying digits, tapping speed, check-lists of words describing various feelings and so on.

Beckett: Can you distinguish in man between amphetamine alone and amphetamine-barbiturate combinations?

Steinberg: Yes.

Silverman: Why were these combinations originally manufactured?

Steinberg: It is difficult to discover this unequivocally, since it happened many years ago. One plausible suggestion about the

* We thank Mr R. D. Porsolt, Mr R. Peto, Mr R. Pollard, Mrs E. Baker, and undergraduate and graduate students of University and Birkbeck Colleges for help with the new experiments described. The work was supported by grant MH-03313 from the National Institute of Health, U.S. Public Health Service.

manufacture of Drinamyl, is that the two smallest tablets of each drug already on the market were given together. This meant that 5 mg dexamphetamine and 32·5 mg amylobarbitone were combined in one tablet giving a ratio of 1:6·5. Why the two drugs were combined in the first place is unclear but it seems to have been the result of psychiatric trial and error (Davidoff and Goodstone, 1942).

Albert: The combination makes a human being "feel better". Does it make the mice feel better?

Steinberg: With appropriate mixtures the animals certainly look alert, purposeful and enterprising (if one may use such language). We filmed the rats, and the effect on walking seemed to stand out above the effects on other kinds of behaviour. This alteration in walking may persist for an hour or more.

Albert: Can you detect the difference between amphetamine alone and the amphetamine-barbiturate combination by the way the rats behave?

Steinberg: Most certainly. With amphetamine alone the animals tend to be "dithery", excited, to rear a great deal, but walk much less.

Boyland: How long after administration of the drugs do you do the test?

Steinberg: After 35 minutes in the rats.

Barnes: This "hangover" effect has also been described by Magos (1969), who found that rats were reacting abnormally four weeks after a single dose of amphetamine. Have any other similar studies of the hangover effect of drugs been recorded?

Steinberg: As far as I know this is the first time that an inverted "U"-shaped dose-response curve has been reproduced without drugs. According to widely held theories (Overton, 1968) the greater the dose of drug at trial I, the less transfer of learning will there be to trial II. If this were so the animals in our experiments which had been given the largest dose would have been expected to behave at trial II like naive controls.

Spinks: Have you been able to reproduce these results so as to show that they were not due to some abnormality in a particular group of animals but to the drugs themselves?

Steinberg: Further work is in progress, but the results I have described have been carefully assessed statistically and found to be valid.

Brimblecombe: Dr Steinberg, I don't think that the disagreement between us is so profound. I agree entirely that in some circumstances behavioural tests are most appropriate, but each type of drug has to be assessed individually. In a screening programme, where one has many compounds to deal with, it is easier and quicker to do the conventional pharmacological or biochemical tests than it is to do the behavioural ones. If one is interested rather more academically in the effects of drugs on behaviour then, naturally, behavioural procedures must be used.

Steinberg: I do not quite agree with your last statement because so much depends on what one is screening for. If the screening is for toxicity or physiological damage then pharmacological test methods may be adequate. But if one is screening in order to extrapolate to effects on human behaviour, then behavioural tests are essential. There may not yet be enough examples of successful extrapolation for us to be sure how useful screening methods which depend on animal behaviour are for this, but that is no reason for not trying to improve and use this sort of approach.

Spinks: I am sure that is right, but what interests me with a completely unknown compound is picking up the first clue that will lead to a justification for the final tests. When we are looking for toxic effects on the liver we can give a large dose and look for a small effect on the liver, realize the risks and then explore them more subtly. Similarly, with many drugs there is no doubt that large doses affect the central nervous system so we can proceed quickly to our more subtle tests. But as Dr Paget has said, for drugs which have fairly subtle central nervous effects in man (cannabis is a good example of this) *ad hoc* clues about these would be difficult to pick up in animals even though large doses of cannabis may show some central nervous effects. If we encounter compounds which have these subtle actions in man it will become increasingly difficult to pick up clues about this in our animal tests.

Weiskrantz: But as we are interested in screening for behavioural effects we can deliberately devise complex multifactorial behavioural screening tests.

Albert: From a practical standpoint transient changes in behaviour are not particularly important, one could simply require a manufacturer to take the agent himself. But it would be a major public health problem if compounds that produce permanent mental disorder were synthesized. Have any compounds producing permanent mental disorders been produced?

Boyland: One example is psychosin.

Albert: Psychosin produces gross brain damage, not the sort of changes that occur in the psychoses or personality disorders.

Steinberg: Has the "hangover" effect been studied after the administration of one or two doses of LSD in animals?

Brimblecombe: We have done this and found no effect.

Kety: It is extremely unlikely that any drug will be found that produces a model of schizophrenia in an animal. Schizophrenia is phenomenologically defined which makes it difficult to dissociate the concept from human behaviour and activity.

Steinberg: It may nevertheless be worth trying to develop testable animal models for some aspects of schizophrenia. This has recently been worked out for schizophrenic "over-arousal" by electrically stimulating the reticular formation in the rat and then using chlorpromazine, an important drug for the treatment of schizophrenia in practice, to counteract the deleterious effects of this electrical brain stimulation (Kornetsky and Eliasson, 1969).

Boyland: A substance may elicit different changes in behaviour in man and in the rat. If there is any effect on behaviour in animals this should serve as a warning that psychologists should investigate the effects in man.

REFERENCES

BESSER, G. M., and STEINBERG, H. (1967). *Thérapie*, **22**, 977–990.

BOHDANECKY, Z., and JARVIK, M. (1967). *Archs int. Pharmacodyn. Ther.*, **170**, 58–65.

BOISSIER, J. R., and SIMON, P. (1962). *Thérapie*, **17**, 1225–1232.

BRADLEY, D. W. M., JOYCE, D., MURPHY, E. H., NASH, B. M., PORSOLT, R. D., SUMMERFIELD, A., and TWYMAN, W. A. (1968). *Nature, Lond.*, **220**, 187–188.

COCHIN, J., and KORNETSKY, C. (1964). *J. Pharmac. exp. Ther.*, **145**, 1–10.

DAVIDOFF, E., and GOODSTONE, G. L. (1942). *Psychiat. Q.*, **16**, 541–548.

DICKINS, D., LADER, M. H., and STEINBERG, H. (1965). *Br. J. Pharmacol. Chemother.*, **24**, 14–23.

DORR, M., JOYCE, D., STEINBERG, H., SUMMERFIELD, A., and TOMKIEWICZ, M. (1970). *Br. J. Pharmac.*, **39**, 208–209 P.

GOLDMAN-EISLER, F. (1968). *Psycholinguistics-Experiments in Spontaneous Speech.* London: Academic Press.

HINDE, R. A. (1966). *Animal Behaviour: A Synthesis of Ethology and Comparative Psychology*. New York: McGraw-Hill.

JOYCE, D. (1970). This volume, pp. 126–140.

JOYCE, D., PORSOLT, R. D., STEINBERG, H., and SUMMERFIELD, A. (1968). *Br. J. Pharmac. Chemother.*, **32,** P 433.

KOECHLIN, B. A., SCHWARTZ, M. A., KROL, G., and OBERHANSLI, W. (1965). *J. Pharmac. exp. Ther.*, **148,** 399–411.

KORNETSKY, C., and BAIN, G. (1968). *Science*, **162,** 1011–1012.

KORNETSKY, C., and ELIASSON, M. (1969). *Science*, **165,** 1273.

MAGOS, L. (1969). *Eur. J. Pharmac.*, **6,** 200–201.

OVERTON, D. A. (1968). In *Psychopharmacology: A Review of Progress*, pp. 918–930, ed. Efron, D. H., Cole, J. O. Levine, J., and Wittenborn, J. R. U.S. Government Printing Office, P.H.S. Publication No. 1836.

PLACIDI, G. F., and Cassano, G. B. (1968). *Int. J. Neuropharmac.*, **7,** 383–389.

ROSS, S., and SCHNITZER, S. B. (1963). *Psychol. Rep.*, **13,** 461–462.

RUSHTON, R., and STEINBERG, H. (1963). *Br. J. Pharmac. Chemother.*, **21,** 295–305.

RUSHTON, R., and STEINBERG, H. (1966). *Nature, Lond.*, **211,** 1312–1313.

RUSHTON, R., and STEINBERG, H. (1967). In *Neuropsychopharmacology*, pp. 464–470, ed. Brill, H., Cole, J. O., Deniker, P., Hippius, H., and Bradley, P. B. Amsterdam: Excerpta Medica Foundation.

RUSHTON, R., STEINBERG, H., and TINSON, C. (1963). *Br. J. Pharmac. Chemother.*, **20,** 99–105.

RUSHTON, R., STEINBERG, H., and TOMKIEWICZ, M. (1968). *Nature, Lond.*, **220,** 885–889.

RUSSELL, R. W. (1960). *U.S. Public Health Service Psychopharmacology Service Center Bulletin*, December, pp. 1–7.

SACHS, E. (1967). In *Comparative Psychopathology: Animal and Human*, pp. 249–304, ed. Zubin, J., and Hunt, H. F. New York: Grune & Stratton.

SHEPHERD, M., LADER, M., and RODNIGHT, R. (1968). *Clinical Psychopharmacology*, London: English Universities Press.

SIEGEL, S. (1956). *Nonparametric Statistics for the Behavioral Sciences*, pp. 184–194. New York: McGraw-Hill.

STEINBERG, H. (1961). *Acta psychol.*, **19,** 771–775.

STERN, M. H. (1960). *Can. J. Psychol.*, **14,** 96–100.

VAN DER KLEIJN, E. (1969). *Archs int. Pharmacodyn. Ther.*, **178,** 193–215.

WECHSLER, D. (1955). *Manual for the Wechsler Adult Intelligence Scale*. New York: Psychological Corp.

WEIL, A. T., and ZINBERG, N. E. (1969). *Nature, Lond.*, **222,** 434–439.

WEIL, A. T., ZINBERG, N. E., and NELSEN, J. M. (1968). *Science*, **162,** 1234–1242.

CHAIRMAN'S CLOSING REMARKS

E. BOYLAND

I AM an admirer of Chekhov. One of Chekhov's characters, Sorin, in *The Seagull* is a man who is full of regrets—*l'homme qui a voulu*—and I have some regrets about this meeting. One is that Dr Horváth was unable to be here. Some of his data on carbon disulphide are shown in Table I, and I think there is a great deal to be said for Dr Horváth's argument about safety.

TABLE I

TOXICITY OF INHALED CARBON DISULPHIDE IN RATS (HORVÁTH)

Concentration $\mu g/l$	
2000	No effect on growth or survival but changed conditioned reflexes
150	No effect on conditioned reflexes but change in EEG in rabbits

I also regret that it has not been possible to define human behaviour or to describe how human performance can be measured. Sir Aubrey Lewis has said that there is no simple way of measuring and defining human behaviour and performance. I wish that there had been time to consider the relevance of simple behavioural tests (Table II) that can be carried out on

TABLE II

ANIMAL BEHAVIOURAL TESTS

Physical effects	Rotor rod or inclined rod
General effects	Observation or Hall's open-field
Spontaneous activity	Activity cage, treadwheel, jiggle cage
Conditioned response	Conditioned avoidance, operant conditioning
Reversal of drug-drug induced behaviour	Convulsions, "waltzing syndrome", sleep, hyperactivity

animals and that might give some indication of how a compound might influence human subjects.

Another Chekhov character, Vershinin, is always looking into the future and in *The Three Sisters* says: "In two or three hundred years life on earth will be unimaginably beautiful, marvellous, and they will see that we were trying to develop for the future". As Dr Paget said, we may have been discussing the subject of this meeting too soon, perhaps because experimental psychologists and clinicians have not yet developed their techniques sufficiently. We ought to test air pollutants such as lead tetraethyl, food additives such as butylated hydroxytoluene, and food contaminants including organochlorine insecticides for behavioural effects. If these compounds give any indications that they are affecting animal behaviour attempts should be made to examine their effects on man.

Is it possible that more epidemiological studies would help to find the environmental factors we are looking for? If more people under treatment were asked about such aspects of their histories as past employment and exposure to mercury, lead or DDT, some indication of the causes of mental disease would be revealed. Another epidemiological approach would be to examine the behaviour and the incidence of disease in workers who are exposed to compounds that are potential hazards. An example of this is the rubber factories where there is an increased incidence of brain tumours. If a chemical is causing cancer of the brain it may also affect behaviour or performance in some way.

Some environmental factors may act as antimetabolites. If these factors give rise to biochemical lesions similar to inherited lesions that are known to be associated with some mental abnormality, they should be put through behavioural tests. The effective substances may not necessarily all be synthetic chemicals; naturally occurring substances found in some moulds and in cannabis are known to affect behaviour.

One of the difficulties in the study of the epidemiology of mental disease is that relatively small numbers of subjects are available. In cancer epidemiology, however, comparison of small groups often gives the best indications of causes. In the rubber industry, for example, indications of the causes of diseases have been found by measuring the difference in the incidence of disease in different parts of the same factory. If large populations are examined the effect of any particular agent becomes diluted and lost.

We have discussed the difference between permanent and reversible effects. If an environmental chemical produces effects which are quickly reversible, then the hazard is less than if they are long-lasting. Behavioural tests on animals should therefore be carried out both during exposure to the test compound and some time later in order to see if the effects of its administration are permanent.

Our discussions over the past two days have posed many questions, although few of the answers to them are yet available. A great deal of research is still needed in the study of behaviour in man and animals.

INDEX*

Acetylcholine, 8
ACTH, 41
S-**Adenosylmethionine,** and
  schizophrenia, 81
Adrenaline, in adaptation to stress,
  106
Aggression,
  effect of nicotine, 28, 30, 59
  effect of benzoctamine, 139
  pheromones and, 146
Alcohol, 192
  changes in attitude and, 141
  effects, 142–143
    convergence–divergence, 135,
      136, 137, 138
    on authoritarianism, 135, 136,
      137
    on experimental conflict, 131–
      137, 141, 142
    on extraversion–introversion,
      127, 135, 138
    on human cooperation, 126–
      143
    on neuroticism, 135, 136, 137
    species differences, 192
  metabolism, 97, 98, 99, 112
Aldolase B, deficiency, 61
Aldosterone, and potassium
  metabolism, 118
Alkohol-Aquivalent, 183
Allobarbitone,
  as standard reference substance,
    184
  effects, 176
Amino acids, and schizophrenia,
  84
Amphetamine, 23, 41
  as standard reference substance,
    184
  brain activity due to, 8
  effects, 110, 166, 175, 176, 180
  excretion and plasma concen-
    tration, 94

**Amphetamine-barbiturate mix-
  tures,** effects of, 201–207
Amylobarbitone,
  effect,
    on shock avoidance response,
      42–51, 52
    on water-approach response,
      42–51
**Anaesthetics stimulating en-
  zyme activity,** 90
Animal tests,
  problems, 15, 23
  to predict effects on man, 6–24,
    25, 58
**Antalgics stimulating enzyme
  activity,** 90
Anticholinergic substances, 7,
  8
Anticholinesterases, effects, 189–
  190
Anticholinesterase inhibitors,
  mental effects, 20
Anticonvulsants, 90
Antidepressants, 91
Antihistamines, 91
Antimetabolites, 212
Aphrodisiacs, in insects, 145
Appetite, effect of pheromones,
  166
Arousal theory, 54, 55
Ascorbic acid, deficiency, 63
  schizophrenia and, 78–79
Atropinase, 71
Atropine, effects, 180, 185
Attitudes, changes in, 141
Authoritarianism, effect of alco-
  hol, 135, 136, 137
Avoidance response, 175

Barbiturates,
  as standard reference substances,
    184, 185
  effects, 41, 176, 177, 179, 192

* Compiled by William Hill.